Table of Contents

Using this Guide

This book is a *guide* for teachers using the Primary Mathematics curriculum. It is designed to help teachers understand the course material, to see how each section fits in with the curriculum as a whole, and to prepare the day's lesson. The course material is divided into 70 sessions. Sessions can be extended by including additional problems from supplementary material, or bringing in review from earlier levels of *Primary Mathematics* as needed.

This guide is designed to be used with both the U.S. edition and the third edition of *Primary Mathematics*. U.S. conventions and spellings are used in this guide, such as using commas for thousands and colons for time, and not using "and" in writing out whole numbers in words. However, any items specific to either edition, such as different answers, different page numbers, and different exercise numbers, are indicated.

Workbook exercises can be gone over in class or assigned as homework.

As this level represents the end of Primary education, the review exercises are extensive, and cover all previous levels of *Primary Mathematics*. If students have difficulty with material in the reviews, you may have to re-teach concepts from earlier levels.

Optional Resources

Extra Practice for Primary Mathematics 6 (U.S. Edition)
This workbook has two to four page exercises covering topics from *Primary Mathematics 6A* and *Primary Mathematics 6B*. The level of difficulty and format of the problems is similar to that of the *Primary Mathematics*. Answers are in the back.

Primary Mathematics Challenging Word Problems 6 (U.S. Edition)
This workbook has word problems only. The problems are topically arranged, with the topics following the same sequence as *Primary Mathematics 6A* and *6B*. Each topic starts with three worked examples, followed by practice problems and then challenge problems. Although the computation skills needed to solve the problems is at the same level as the corresponding *Primary Mathematics*, the problem solving techniques necessary in the challenge section are sometimes more advanced, with the problems requiring more steps to solve. It is a good source, though, of extra word problems that can be discussed in class or of enrichment problems for more capable students. Answers are in the back.

Primary Mathematics Intensive Practice 6B (U.S. Edition)
This workbook has one set of problems for each topic in *Primary Mathematics*. Each topical exercise has questions of varying levels of difficulty, but the difficulty level is usually higher than that in the *Primary Mathematics* textbook or workbook. Some of the word problems are quite challenging and require the students to extend their understanding of the concepts and develop problem solving abilities. There is also a section called "Take the Challenge!" with non-routine problems that can be used to further develop students' problem solving abilities. Answers are located in the back.

Wiggle Woods CD-ROM

This CD-ROM contains learning activities and two games. The name of the program refers to the bug theme. Topics covered include material from both Primary Mathematics 5 and 6. The following chart correlates the different activities to the appropriate part of *Primary Mathematics 6B*.

Primary Mathematics 6B	***Wiggle Woods Primary Six***
Unit US2 3d1 – Circles Part 2 – Circumference	Circles: Learn and Explore 1 Activity
Part 3 – Area	Circles: Learn and Explore 2 Activity Challenge
Unit US4 3d3 – Volume Part 1 – Solving Problems	Game 2

Blank page

US edition: Unit 1 – Fractions

Objectives

- Divide a whole number or a fraction by a fraction.
- Divide a fraction by a whole number.
- Do mixed operations which involve all four operations and fractions with and without parentheses.
- Solve multi-step problems which involve fractions.

Suggested number of sessions: 13

	Objectives	Textbook	Workbook	Activities
Part 1 : Division				**6 sessions**
1	▪ Divide a whole number by a unit fraction.	p. 6 p. 7, tasks 1-3	Ex. 1	1.1a
2	▪ Divide a fraction by a whole number.	pp. 7-8, tasks 4-6	Ex. 2	1.1b
3	▪ Divide a fraction by a unit fraction.	p. 8, tasks 7-9		1.1c
4	▪ Divide a whole number by a fraction.	p. 9, tasks 10, 11(a)-11(b), 12(a)-12(c)		1.1d
5	▪ Divide a fraction by a fraction.	p. 9, tasks 10-12	Ex. 3	1.1e
6	▪ Practice.	p. 10, Practice 1A		1.1f
Part 2 : Order of Operations				**3 sessions**
7	▪ Do mixed operations which involve addition and subtraction with fractions, without parentheses. ▪ Do mixed operations which involve multiplication and division with fractions, without parentheses.	pp. 12-13, tasks 1-7 p. 15, #1, practice 1B	Ex. 4	1.2a
8	▪ Do mixed operations which involve all four operations with fractions, without parentheses.	p. 11 pp. 13-14 tasks 8-13 p. 15, #2, practice 1B	Ex. 5	1.2b
9	▪ Do mixed operations involving all four operations with fractions, with parentheses.	p. 14, tasks 14-15 p. 15, #3-5, practice 1B	Ex. 6	1.2c
Part 3 : Word Problems				**4 sessions**
10	▪ Solve word problems which involve fractions, using pictorial models.	pp. 16-17, tasks 1-2	Ex. 7	1.3a
11		pp. 18-19, tasks 3-6	Ex. 8	1.3b
12 13	▪ Practice	p. 20, Practice 1C p. 21, Practice 1D		1.3c

Part 1: Division — 6 sessions

Objectives

- Divide a whole number by a unit fraction.
- Divide a fraction by a whole number.
- Divide a fraction by a unit fraction.
- Divide a whole number by a fraction.
- Divide a fraction by a fraction.

Materials

- Fraction circles

Homework

- Workbook Exercise 1
- Workbook Exercise 2
- Workbook Exercise 3

Notes

In *Primary Mathematics 4A*, students learned how to multiply a fraction by a whole number. In *Primary Mathematics 5A*, they learned how to multiply a fraction by a fraction, relate division to fractions, and divide a fraction by a whole number.

In this section, students review dividing a fraction by a whole number, and also learn to divide a fraction by a fraction, starting with division by a unit fraction (a fraction with 1 in its numerator).

Division of whole numbers can be interpreted in two contexts: sharing or grouping.

In grouping, we are given the total number and the number that goes into each part, and want to find how many parts there are. In $8 \div 2$, we are finding how many 2's there are in 8, or 8 is how many 2's, that is, what number times 2 is 8?

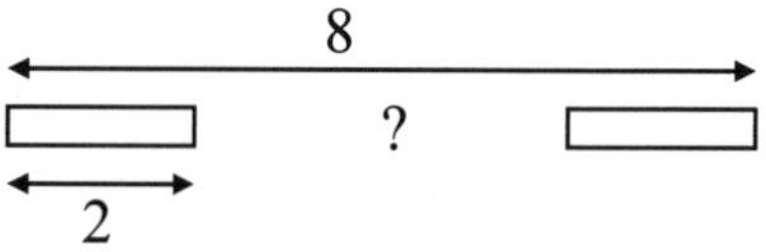

$8 \div 2 = ?$ How many 2's in 8?, or, 8 is how many 2's?, or $? \times 2 = 8$

$8 \div 2 = \mathbf{4}$ There are **4** 2's in 8.

In sharing, we are given a total number and the number of parts, and need to find the value in each part. In $8 \div 2$, we are finding the "what" of "8 is 2 of what?"

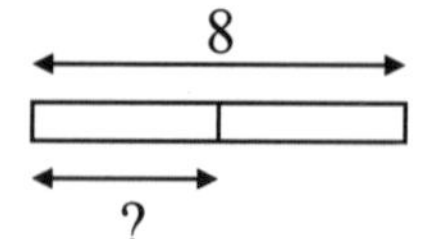

$8 \div 2 = ?$ 8 is 2 of what? Or, $2 \times ? = 8$

$8 \div 2 = \mathbf{4}$ 8 is 2 **4**'s

Division of fractions can also be interpreted in two contexts:

Total ÷ ____ = ?

means

How many ___'s are there in the total? (? × ___ = total)

or

The total is ___ of what? (total = ___ of ? or, total = ___ × ?

Examples:

1. $8 \div \frac{1}{2} = ?$

(a) How many $\frac{1}{2}$'s are there in 8?

(e.g.: There are 8 apples. Each person gets $\frac{1}{2}$ of an apple. How many people are there?)

If we divide 8 by $\frac{1}{2}$, we can think of this as putting $\frac{1}{2}$ into each part (grouping by $\frac{1}{2}$), and finding how many parts there are. Since there are 2 halves in one whole, there would be 2 × 8 halves in 8 wholes.

1 whole ⟶ 2 halves
8 wholes ⟶ 8 × 2 halves

So, the answer can be found by multiplying by 2:

$8 \div \frac{1}{2} = 8 \times 2 = 16$

There are 16 halves in 8.

(b) 8 is $\frac{1}{2}$ of what?

(e.g.: If half of a carton of milk is 8 cups, how many cups are in the whole carton?)

If half of something is 8, then

$\frac{1}{2} \longrightarrow 8$

$1 \longrightarrow 8 \times 2$

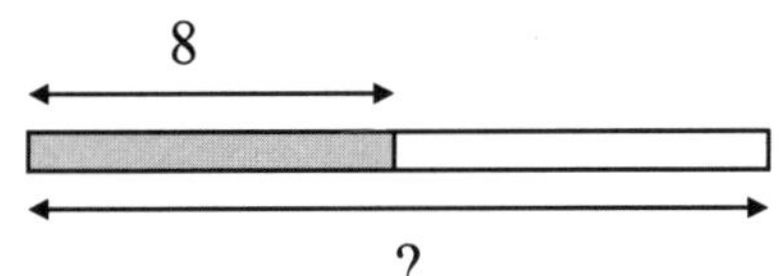

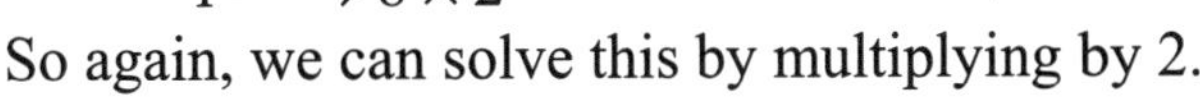

So again, we can solve this by multiplying by 2.

$8 \div \frac{1}{2} = 8 \times 2 = 16$

8 is half of 16

2 is the *reciprocal* of $\frac{1}{2}$. The product of a number and its reciprocal is 1: $2 \times \frac{1}{2} = 1$

To divide by $\frac{1}{2}$, we multiply by its reciprocal, 2.

2. $\frac{1}{2} \div \frac{1}{4} = ?$

(a) How many $\frac{1}{4}$'s are there in $\frac{1}{2}$?

We can interpret this as starting with $\frac{1}{2}$, putting $\frac{1}{4}$ into each part, and finding out how many parts there are. This is illustrated in the textbook on p. 8.
The same answer is found if we multiply $\frac{1}{2}$ by 4.

$$\frac{1}{2} \div \frac{1}{4} = \frac{1}{2} \times 4 = 2.$$

There are **2** $\frac{1}{4}$ parts in $\frac{1}{2}$.

(b) $\frac{1}{2}$ is $\frac{1}{4}$ of what?"

To diagram this, we can draw a bar to show the "what", divide it in fourths, and mark each fourth as $\frac{1}{2}$. To find the value for what, we multiply $\frac{1}{2}$ by 4.

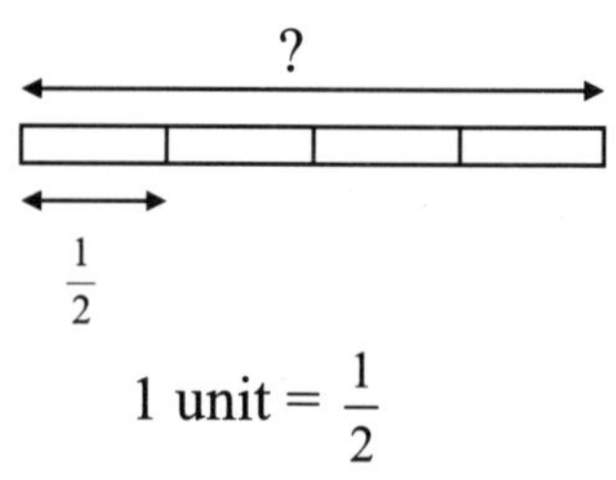

1 unit = $\frac{1}{2}$

4 units = $\frac{1}{2} \times 4$

$$\frac{1}{2} \div \frac{1}{4} = \frac{1}{2} \times 4 = 2.$$

$\frac{1}{2}$ is $\frac{1}{4}$ of 2

4 is the *reciprocal* of $\frac{1}{4}$. To divide by $\frac{1}{4}$ we multiply by its reciprocal.

3. $\frac{1}{3} \div \frac{2}{9} = ?$

(a) How many $\frac{2}{9}$'s are there in $\frac{1}{3}$?

We need to put $\frac{2}{9}$ into each part and then find out how many parts make up $\frac{1}{3}$.

To diagram this, we can divide a bar into thirds, mark 1 of the thirds, draw a bar under that, which we divide into ninths, and see how many $\frac{2}{9}$'s of them correspond to a third. We know there are three ninths in a third, so 3 units in the second bar would be the same length as 1 unit in the first bar.

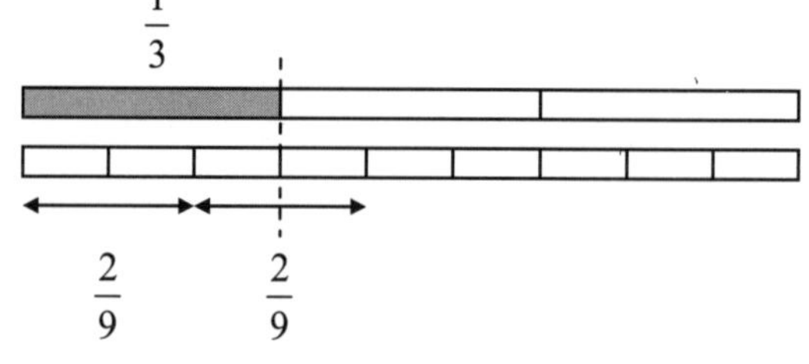

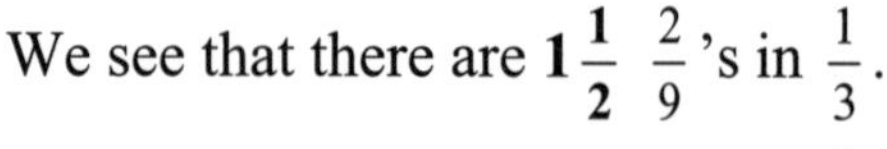
We see that there are $\mathbf{1\frac{1}{2}}$ $\frac{2}{9}$'s in $\frac{1}{3}$.

If we multiply by the reciprocal, $\frac{9}{2}$, we get the same answer: $\frac{1}{3} \div \frac{2}{9} = \frac{1}{3} \times \frac{9}{2} = \frac{3}{2} = 1\frac{1}{2}$

(b) $\frac{1}{3}$ is $\frac{2}{9}$ of what?

To diagram this, we can draw a bar to show the "what", divide it in ninths, mark two of the ninths as $\frac{1}{3}$. Each ninth is a unit, nine units is the total. To find 9 units, we first divide by 2 to get one unit, and then multiply by 9 to get 9 units. This is the same as multiplying $\frac{1}{3}$ by $\frac{9}{2}$.

The total is $\frac{3}{2}$.

$\frac{1}{3}$ is $\frac{2}{9}$ of $\frac{3}{2}$

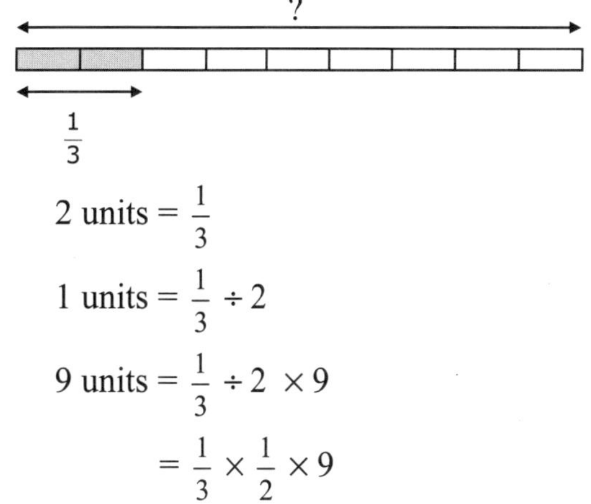

$$2 \text{ units} = \frac{1}{3}$$

$$1 \text{ units} = \frac{1}{3} \div 2$$

$$9 \text{ units} = \frac{1}{3} \div 2 \times 9$$

$$= \frac{1}{3} \times \frac{1}{2} \times 9$$

$$= \frac{1}{3} \times \frac{9}{2}$$

$$= \frac{3}{2}$$

From this, we can also see that to divide by $\frac{2}{9}$, we multiply by its reciprocal.

$$\frac{1}{3} \div \frac{2}{9} = \frac{1}{3} \times \frac{9}{2} = \frac{3}{2} = 1\frac{1}{2}$$

In all these cases, division is the same as multiplying by the reciprocal. This is true even when we divide by a whole number: $8 \div 2 = 8 \times \frac{1}{2}$ or $\frac{1}{8} \div 2 = \frac{1}{8} \times \frac{1}{2}$.

You may have learned that to divide by a fraction you "invert and multiply." It is important that students understand what is happening in division of fractions through the use of diagrams so that they can apply the principles to word problems, rather than simply memorizing "invert and multiply".

Activity 1.1a **Divide a whole number by a unit fraction**

1. Discuss the division of a whole number by a unit fraction as "How many ___'s are there in the total?"
    - Write the division expression $6 \div 2 = 3$ and illustrate its solution with circles as a grouping problem.
    - Tell students you have 6 oranges (apples, pizzas, cakes…) and want to put them into groups of 2. How many groups will there be? There will be 3 groups. There are 3 groups of 2 in 6, or there are 3 twos in 6. We can think of this division problem as finding how many groups of 2 make 6.

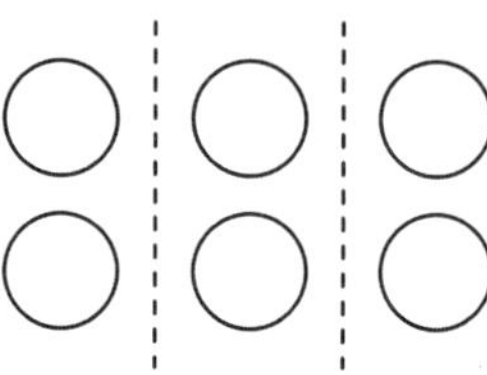

$6 \div 2 = ?$
How many 2's are in 6?
There are 3 groups of 2.
$6 \div 2 = 3$

- Now write the expression $6 \div \frac{1}{2}$.
- Tell students that now we want to put $\frac{1}{2}$ an orange into each group. Divide each of the 6 circles into half. How many groups will there be? There will be 12 groups. There are 12 halves in 6.
- We divided each whole into $\frac{1}{2}$, so for each whole we formed 2 groups. For 6 wholes, we formed 6×2 groups. So $6 \div \frac{1}{2}$ is the same as 6×2.
- Point out that when you divide by a number less than 1, the answer (quotient) will be larger than the number you are dividing. 12 is larger than 6.
- Remind your students that division is related to multiplication.
    - So for $6 \div 2 =$ ____, we can think: ____ $\times 2 = 6$, or, how many 2's are there in 6.
    - For $6 \div \frac{1}{2} =$ ____, we can think: how many $\frac{1}{2}$'s are there in 6?

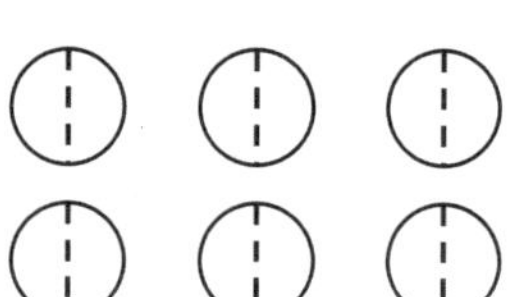

$6 \div \frac{1}{2} = ?$

How many $\frac{1}{2}$'s are in 6?

There are 12 groups of $\frac{1}{2}$ in 6.

$6 \div \frac{1}{2} = 12$

$6 \div \frac{1}{2} = 12 = 6 \times 2$

2. Discuss division of a whole number by a unit fraction as "The total is ___ of what?"
    - Tell students that $6 \div 2 = 3$ can also mean that we have 2 parts and want to find the value in each part. That is, $6 = 2 \times$ ____, or, 6 is 2 of *what*?
    - Now, tell students: we are told that $\frac{1}{2}$ of a container is 6 liters.
    - Draw a bar diagram on the board to illustrate this.
    - We want to find the amount in the whole container. That is, $\frac{1}{2}$ of *what* is 6, or $\frac{1}{2} \times$ ____ $= 6$. This problem

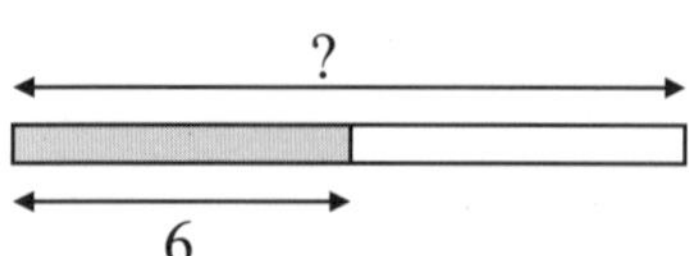

can also be written as a division problem:

$6 \div \frac{1}{2} = \_\_\_\_$.

- The answer is 12, and we can also find the answer by multiplying 6 by 2. So $6 \div \frac{1}{2} = 6 \times 2$
- Students can solve this in ways similar to many fraction problems they have seen earlier (if they did earlier levels of *Primary Mathematics*). For example: "Mary spent half of her money on a purse which cost $6. How much money did she have?" They have been solving this kind of problem with units. Now they can use division of a fraction to solve the problem. Often, though, a problem such as this is easier to understand and solve using diagrams and units.

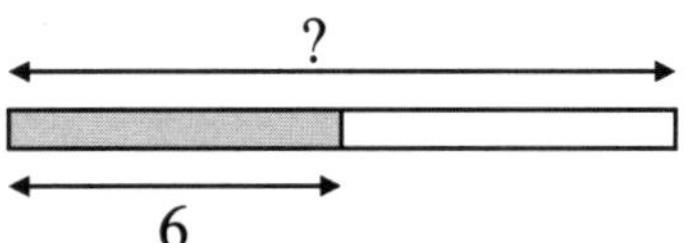

$6 \div \frac{1}{2} = ?$

6 is half of what?

$6 \div \frac{1}{2} = 12$

$6 \div \frac{1}{2} = 12 = 6 \times 2$

3. Discuss **p. 6 in the textbook** and **tasks 1-2, textbook p. 7**
   - You may want to tell students that 3 is the *reciprocal* of $\frac{1}{3}$. When a number is multiplied by its reciprocal, the answer is 1.
   - You may also want to point out that the expression in 2(a), $1 \div \frac{1}{4}$, could have been written to answer a question where we are asked to find how many fourths there are in 1, or to find out what 1 is a fourth of. The answer in both cases is 4, and we can find it by multiplying 1 by the reciprocal of $\frac{1}{4}$, which is 4.

4. Ask students to do **task 3, textbook p. 7** and share their solutions.
   - You may want to ask students to make up word problems to go along with the expressions.

Workbook Exercise 1

Activity 1.1b **Divide a fraction by a whole number**

1. Illustrate dividing a fraction by a whole number.
   - Ask students to describe what is happening when we divide 8 by 4. We are finding a fourth of 8. So $8 \div 4$ is the same as $\frac{1}{4}$ of 8, or $\frac{8}{4}$, or $8 \times \frac{1}{4}$.
   - Discuss **task 4, textbook p. 7**. Lead students to see that when we divide $\frac{1}{2}$ by 4, we are finding $\frac{1}{4}$ of $\frac{1}{2}$, so $\frac{1}{2} \div 4$ is the same as $\frac{1}{2} \times \frac{1}{4}$.

$8 \div 4 = 8 \times \frac{1}{4} = 2$

$\frac{1}{2} \div 4 = \frac{1}{2} \times \frac{1}{4} = \frac{1}{8}$

- Point out that in these problems, we are dividing by a whole number. The answer is smaller than the number we are dividing. $\frac{1}{4}$ is smaller than $\frac{1}{2}$.

2. Discuss **task 5, textbook p. 8.**
   - Have students illustrate the two problems using bar diagrams.

3. Have students do **task 6, textbook p. 8.**
   - You can ask students to make up word problems that would go along with the expressions.

Workbook Exercise 2

Activity 1.1c **Divide a fraction by a unit fraction**

1. Illustrate dividing a fraction by a unit fraction when the quotient is a whole number.
   - Tell students you have a half of a liter of juice, and you want to pour it into cups which each hold a quarter of a liter. Or, in US standard measurements, you have half a quart of juice and want to divide it into cups (8 oz = a quarter of a quart = 1 cup). Draw a picture, marking the container as a half a liter or half a quart. How many cups will you need? Students should be able to intuitively determine that you need 2 cups.
   - Write the equation $\frac{1}{2} \div \frac{1}{4} = 2$.
   - Point out that we are dividing by a fraction, so the answer is larger than the number we are dividing. 2 is larger than $\frac{1}{2}$.
   - Show that we get the same answer by multiplying $\frac{1}{2}$ by 4.

$$\frac{1}{2} \div \frac{1}{4} = 2$$
$$\frac{1}{2} \times 4 = 2$$
$$\frac{1}{2} \div \frac{1}{4} = \frac{1}{2} \times 4 = 2$$

   - Tell students that they have determined that there are 2 fourths in a half.
   - Rewrite the division as a multiplication equation.

$$\frac{1}{2} \div \frac{1}{4} = \mathbf{2}$$
$$\mathbf{2} \times \frac{1}{4} = \frac{1}{2}$$

   - Discuss **task 7, textbook p. 8**. This is the same problem, illustrated instead with bars. The sentence in the thought bubble can be confusing. We are not dividing $\frac{1}{2}$ by quartering it up. It would be a good idea to re-word this as "Divide $\frac{1}{2}$ into fourths. There are two $\frac{1}{4}$'s." rather than using the word "quarters".
   - Now, tell students you have a half a liter of juice, and you pour it into another container, and see that it fills the other container $\frac{1}{4}$ of the way up. Draw a picture of a container that is $\frac{1}{4}$ full and mark the amount as $\frac{1}{4}$ liter.

- Ask students for the capacity of the larger container. They should be able to tell you it is 2 liters.
- So $\frac{1}{2}$ is $\frac{1}{4}$ of 2. Remind students that division is the opposite of multiplication. We can write the problem as $\frac{1}{2} \div \frac{1}{4} = 2$.
- Draw a bar diagram to illustrate this problem.
- Again, we see that $\frac{1}{2} \div \frac{1}{4} = \frac{1}{2} \times 4$.

$\frac{1}{2} = \frac{1}{4} \times ?$

$\frac{1}{2} \div \frac{1}{4} = ?$

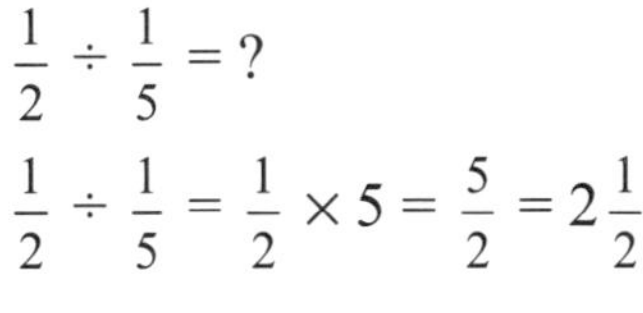

$\frac{1}{2} \div \frac{1}{4} = \frac{1}{2} \times 4$

2. Discuss **task 8, textbook p. 8.**
   - Have students illustrate the two problems using bar diagrams.
   - Task 8(a) can be drawn either as finding the number of thirds in two thirds, or as two thirds is a third of what?
   - 8(b) can be illustrated either as finding the number of sixths in two thirds, or as two thirds is a sixth of what?

3. Illustrate dividing a fraction by a unit fraction when the answer is not a whole number.
   - Write the problem $\frac{1}{2} \div \frac{1}{5} = ?$
   - We can interpret this as how many fifths there are in a half. Have students solve the problem by multiplying $\frac{1}{2}$ by 5. We find that there are $2\frac{1}{2}$ fifths in $\frac{1}{2}$.
   - Does this make sense? Show students how to diagram what is happening with a bar diagram. First show a bar divided in half. Then draw another bar under it and ask them how we can divide it up into fifths to be proportional to the other bar. If we divide it into tenths, 5 of them are one half. Draw a third bar showing fifths (one fifth for every two tenths). There are $2\frac{1}{2}$ of these fifths in $\frac{1}{2}$.

$\frac{1}{2} \div \frac{1}{5} = ?$

$\frac{1}{2} \div \frac{1}{5} = \frac{1}{2} \times 5 = \frac{5}{2} = 2\frac{1}{2}$

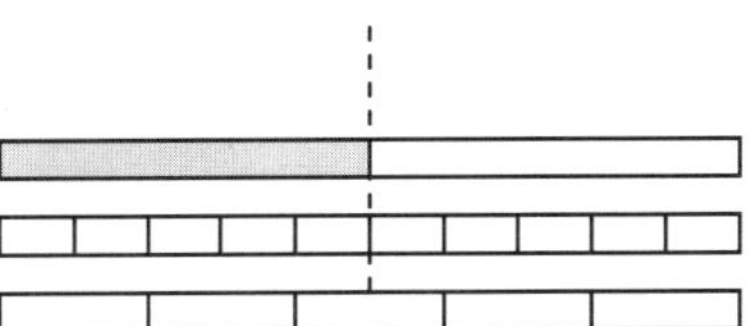

- We can also interpret $\frac{1}{2} \div \frac{1}{5} = ?$ as $\frac{1}{2}$ is $\frac{1}{5}$ of what?
Draw a bar diagram to illustrate the problem. To answer this, we need to multiply $\frac{1}{2}$ by 5, and we get an answer of $= 2\frac{1}{2}$. So here again we see that $\frac{1}{2} \div \frac{1}{5} = \frac{1}{2} \times 5$

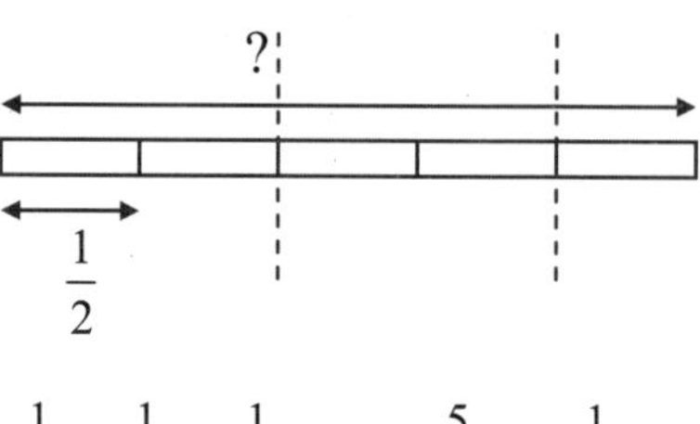

$$\frac{1}{2} \div \frac{1}{5} = \frac{1}{2} \times 5 = \frac{5}{2} = 2\frac{1}{2}$$

4. Have students do **task 8, textbook p. 8.**

Activity 1.1d **Divide a whole number by a fraction**

1. Illustrate dividing a whole number by a fraction where the quotient is a whole number. Students can work in groups for this activity.
   - Provide students with 6 sheets of paper.
     - Tell students that each sheet of paper is one whole. They can imagine each sheet to be a small cake, or a square pizza, or whatever appeals.
     - Write the problem $6 \div \frac{3}{4} = ?$ on the board.
     $$6 \div \frac{3}{4} = ?$$
     - Tell them that 6 cakes were divided among some friends so that each person got $\frac{3}{4}$ of a "cake".
     - Ask them to find out how many friends there are (8). When they are done, ask them to explain how they solved the problem.
     - Lead students to see that since each person must get a certain number of fourths, the "cakes" had to be divided first into fourths. There are $6 \times 4 = 24$ fourths. Then to give each person three of them, each fourth had to be divided into groups of 3.
     $$\frac{6 \times 4}{3} = 6 \times \frac{4}{3} = 6 \div \frac{3}{4}$$
     $$6 \div \frac{3}{4} = 6 \times \frac{4}{3} = \frac{24}{3} = 8$$
     - We multiplied the number of papers (6) by 4 and then divided that total by 3. To divide by $\frac{3}{4}$, we had to multiply by $\frac{4}{3}$.
     - Here, in dividing by a fraction, the answer is larger than the number we are dividing.
   - Discuss **task 10, textbook p. 9**.

2. Illustrate dividing a whole number by a fraction where the answer is not a whole number.
   - Have students repeat the activity above, with 5 sheets of paper. That is, they need to find how many $\frac{3}{4}$'s there are in 5 by dividing the papers into fourths and then grouping by 3 so that each group has three fourths in it.
   - Write the problem $5 \div \frac{3}{4} = ?$ on the board.
   - Students will find that they can make 6 groups of three fourths, and have 2 fourths left over.

- Ask them: what fraction of a group do those two fourths represent? If each group normally has three fourth in it, then the remaining two fourths is $\frac{2}{3}$ of a group of three fourths. So they have $6\frac{2}{3}$ groups. There are $6\frac{2}{3}$ three fourths in 5.

$5 \div \frac{3}{4} = ?$

$5 \div \frac{3}{4} = 6\frac{2}{3}$

- Have students find $5 \times \frac{4}{3}$, and write the answer as a mixed number. They will find that they get the same answer. So $5 \div \frac{3}{4} = 5 \times \frac{4}{3}$.

$5 \times \frac{4}{3} = \frac{20}{3} = 6\frac{2}{3}$

$5 \div \frac{3}{4} = 5 \times \frac{4}{3}$

- Have students solve some other problems that involve division of a whole number by a fraction using both methods; grouping fractions of paper sheets or strips, and multiplying by the reciprocal. If a group is not full, they need to find the unfilled group as a fraction of a filled group.

3. Have students do **tasks 11(a), 11(b), 12(a), 12(b), and 12(c), textbook p. 9.**

4. Relate division of a whole number by a fraction to bar models that students have previously done.
   - Write the problem shown here on the board and have students solve by using bar models. Write the equation for finding the value of 1 unit, then 4 units, as shown here.
     Tell students that what we are trying to find the answer to "6 is $\frac{3}{4}$ of ?", or, $6 \div \frac{3}{4} = ?$

     6 is $\frac{3}{4}$ of 8.
   - Point out that $\frac{6}{3} \times 4$ is the same as $6 \times \frac{4}{3}$. So here again, we find that $6 \div \frac{3}{4} = 6 \times \frac{4}{3} = 8$, and that we have been doing division of a whole number by a fraction all along, as early as *Primary Mathematics 4A*.

> Marie had some ribbon. She used $\frac{3}{4}$ of it for a collage. The piece used for the collage was 6 cm long. How long was the ribbon at first?

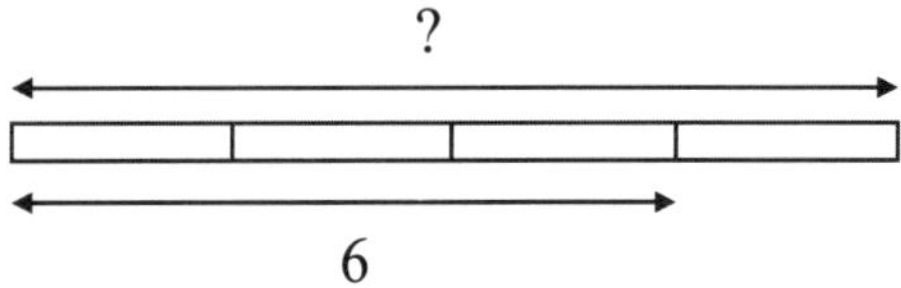

3 units = 6 cm

1 unit = $\frac{6}{3}$ cm

4 units = $\frac{6}{3} \times 4 = 8$

The ribbon was 8 cm long.

Activity 1.1e **Divide a fraction by a fraction**

1. Illustrate dividing a whole number by a fraction where the answer is a whole number.
   - Provide students with a sheet of paper.
   - Have them fold it into quarters, cut out the quarters, and discard one quarter.
   - Write the problem $\frac{3}{4} \div \frac{3}{8} = ?$ on the board.
   - Ask students to find how many $\frac{3}{8}$'s there are in $\frac{3}{4}$. They will have to further divide the paper into eighths and then group the eighths by 3. They will have 2 groups. So $\frac{3}{4} \div \frac{3}{8} = 2$; there are two $\frac{3}{8}$'s in $\frac{3}{4}$.
   - Tell student that we have already learned that $3 \div \frac{3}{8} = 3 \times \frac{8}{3}$. Let us see if $\frac{3}{4} \div \frac{3}{8} = \frac{3}{4} \times \frac{8}{3}$. Write $\frac{3}{4} \times \frac{8}{3}$ on the board and have students solve it. The answer is the same.
   - Point out that when we simplify the fraction, we are essentially doubling each of the $\frac{3}{4}$ (as we did when cutting the fourths into eighths) and then putting each of the six eighths into groups of 2.

$\frac{3}{4} \div \frac{3}{8} = ?$

$\frac{3}{4} \div \frac{3}{8} = 2$

$\frac{3}{4} \times \frac{8}{3} = \frac{3}{\cancel{4}_1} \times \frac{\cancel{8}^2}{3} = 2$

$\frac{3}{4} \div \frac{3}{8} = \frac{3}{4} \times \frac{8}{3} = 2$

2. Illustrate dividing a whole number by a fraction where the answer is not a whole number.
   - Again, provide students with a sheet of paper and have them fold it into quarters, cut out the quarters, and discard one quarter.
   - Write the problem $\frac{3}{4} \div \frac{5}{16} = ?$ on the board.
   - Ask students to find how many $\frac{5}{16}$'s there are in $\frac{3}{4}$.
   - This time they need to divide each fourth into four parts. They will now have $3 \times 4 = 12$ parts. Each part is $\frac{1}{16}$ of the whole.
   - If they put them into groups of 5, they will have 2 whole groups and one group of 2. Ask them to find that group as a fraction of a whole group; it is $\frac{2}{5}$ of a whole group. So they have $2\frac{2}{5}$ groups. So $\frac{3}{4} \div \frac{5}{16} = 2\frac{2}{5}$. There are $2\frac{2}{5}$ $\frac{5}{16}$ in $\frac{3}{4}$.

$\frac{3}{4} \div \frac{5}{16} = ?$

$\frac{3}{4} \div \frac{5}{16} = 2\frac{2}{5}$

- Now have them solve the problem $\frac{3}{4} \times \frac{16}{5}$. The answer is the same, and the process is similar to what they did with the paper pieces.

$$\frac{3}{4} \times \frac{16}{5} = \frac{3}{\cancel{4}_1} \times \frac{\cancel{16}^4}{5} = \frac{12}{5} = 2\frac{2}{5}$$

$$\frac{3}{4} \div \frac{5}{16} = \frac{3}{4} \times \frac{16}{5} = 2\frac{2}{5}$$

3. Have students do **tasks 11(c), 11(d), 12(d), 12(e), and 12(f), textbook p. 9.**

Workbook Exercise 3

Activity 1.1f **Practice, word problems**

1. Summarize the unit so far.
   - Tell students that $\frac{16}{5}$ is called the *reciprocal* of $\frac{5}{16}$. When a number is multiplied by its reciprocal, the product is 1. $\frac{5}{16} \times \frac{16}{5} = 1$.
   - Ask students for reciprocals of various fractions, including whole numbers. $\frac{1}{4}$ is the reciprocal of 4, since $4 \times \frac{1}{4} = 1$.
   - In all the cases we have looked at, division is the same as multiplying by the reciprocal, even when dividing a whole number by a whole number. List the different cases.

$$6 \div 2 = 6 \times \frac{1}{2} = 3$$

$$\frac{1}{2} \div 4 = \frac{1}{2} \times \frac{1}{4} = \frac{1}{8}$$

$$6 \div \frac{1}{2} = 6 \times 2 = 12$$

$$\frac{1}{2} \div \frac{1}{4} = \frac{1}{2} \times 4 = 2$$

$$\frac{1}{2} \div \frac{1}{5} = \frac{1}{2} \times 5 = \frac{5}{2} = 2\frac{1}{2}$$

$$6 \div \frac{3}{4} = 6 \times \frac{4}{3} = 8$$

$$5 \div \frac{3}{4} = 5 \times \frac{4}{3} = \frac{20}{3} = 6\frac{2}{3}$$

$$\frac{3}{4} \div \frac{3}{8} = \frac{3}{4} \times \frac{8}{3} = 2$$

$$\frac{3}{4} \div \frac{5}{16} = \frac{3}{4} \times \frac{16}{5} = \frac{12}{5} = 2\frac{2}{5}$$

2. Have students do **Practice 1A, textbook p. 10** and share their solutions.
   - Note that the word problems in this practice are not all division problems. Students need to read the problem carefully. If they try to answer the last two as division problems, have them diagram these. They can draw bar diagrams or other diagrams for any of the word problems.

Part 2: Order of Operations — 3 sessions

Objectives

- Do mixed operations involving addition and subtraction with fractions, following rules for order of operations.

Homework

- Workbook Exercise 4
- Workbook Exercise 5
- Workbook Exercise 6

Notes

In *Primary Mathematics 5A*, students learned how to solve expressions which involve whole numbers with more than two terms, using rules for order of operation. This is extended here to fractions.

If students did not do *Primary Mathematics 5A* and have not had problems where they must follow order of operation in whatever curriculum they used before, teach order of operations with whole numbers before proceeding. You can use part 6 of unit 1 of *Primary Mathematics 5A*.

If the problem does not have parentheses to indicate which operation is done first, then we follow the convention of first doing multiplication or division from left to right first, and then addition and subtraction from left to right.

Addition and multiplication are commutative (a + b = b + a). If the problem only contains addition or multiplication, the terms can be added or multiplied in any order. Since division of fractions involves multiplication by the reciprocal, once all the division has been changed into multiplication, the problem can be done in any order, and can be simplified in any order.

$$\frac{3}{5} \times \frac{4}{9} \div \frac{3}{10} \div 2 = \frac{\cancel{3}^1}{\cancel{5}_1} \times \frac{4}{9} \times \frac{\cancel{10}^{\cancel{2}^1}}{\cancel{3}_1} \times \frac{1}{\cancel{2}_1} = \frac{4}{9}$$

If the problem has multiplication and division along with addition or subtraction, the multiplication and division part can be solved together as a unit, if all the division operations are changed into multiplication by the reciprocal. For example:

$$2 \times 3 \div 9 + \frac{1}{2} = \underline{2 \times \cancel{3}^1 \times \frac{1}{\cancel{9}_3}} + \frac{1}{2} = \frac{2}{3} + \frac{1}{2} = \frac{4}{6} + \frac{3}{6} = \frac{7}{6}$$

It is not necessary to require students to show every single step in their solution if they consistently get the right answer. Mental math is encouraged in this curriculum. If there are several multiplication or division operations separated by an addition or subtraction operation, they can be recorded in the same step, rather than first one and then the other, since they do not affect each other. For example:

$$4 \div \frac{2}{5} + 5 \div \frac{5}{8} = \underline{\cancel{4}^{2} \times \frac{5}{\cancel{2}_{1}}} + \underline{\cancel{5}^{1} \times \frac{8}{\cancel{5}_{1}}} = 10 + 8 = 18$$

You can also let students cut down on the number of steps recorded by showing equivalent fractions in one step, rather than two. For example, for

$$\frac{1}{3} + \frac{1}{2} = \frac{2}{6} + \frac{3}{6} = \frac{5}{6} \text{ we can write } \frac{\cancel{1}^{2}}{\cancel{3}_{6}} + \frac{\cancel{1}^{3}}{\cancel{2}_{6}} = \frac{5}{6}$$

However, if students get confused and start multiplying instead of adding, or consistently get wrong answers, require them to show intermediate steps.

If the expression contains parentheses, the rules for order of operations are applied first to the expression in parentheses in order to replace it with a single term, and then to the entire expression.

$$\frac{2}{5} \times \underline{(18 - 3)} + \frac{3}{10} = \underline{\frac{2}{\cancel{5}_{1}} \times \cancel{15}^{3}} + \frac{3}{10} = 6 + \frac{3}{10} = 6\frac{3}{10}$$

Activity 1.2a **Mixed operations with just two operations**

1. Discuss addition and subtraction of fractions when there are more than two terms.
   - Write the expression 11 + 6 + 4 on the board.
   - Remind students that since we can do addition in any order, we can first add 6 and 4 to solve this expression.

     $11 + 6 + 4 = 11 + 10 = 21$
   - Write the expression 11 – 6 + 4 on the board. Remind students that subtraction cannot be done in any order, 11 – 6 is not the same as 6 – 11.

     $11 - 6 + 4$

     $11 - 6 + 4 \neq 11 - 10$
   - We add and subtract from left to right. We can't first add 6 and 4 to get 10, and then subtract 10 from 11. We must first subtract 6 from 11, and then add 4 to 5. We can change the order of operations only if we keep the minus sign with the number following it. So we can add 4 to 11 first, and then subtract 6 from that sum.

     $11 - 6 + 4 = 5 + 4 = 9$

     $11 - 6 + 4 = 11 + 4 - 6 = 15 - 6$
   - Refer to **task 1, textbook p. 12**. Write the problem on the board.
   - We need to first subtract $\frac{1}{2}$ from $\frac{3}{4}$. We could change $\frac{1}{2}$ to $\frac{2}{4}$ and subtract that from $\frac{3}{4}$ to get $\frac{1}{4}$, then add $\frac{1}{3}$ by finding equivalent fractions for both.

     $$\begin{aligned}\frac{3}{4} - \frac{1}{2} + \frac{1}{3} &= \frac{3}{4} - \frac{2}{4} + \frac{1}{3} \\ &= \frac{1}{4} + \frac{1}{3} \\ &= \frac{3}{12} + \frac{4}{12} \\ &= \frac{7}{12}\end{aligned}$$
   - Ask students if they can think of an easier way to do this problem, with fewer steps. We can find equivalent factions for all three by using a common multiple of 4, 2, and 3. If we use the lowest common multiple, (12 instead of, for example, 24) we don't have to simplify the answer as often.

     $$\begin{aligned}\frac{3}{4} - \frac{1}{2} + \frac{1}{3} &= \frac{9}{12} - \frac{6}{12} + \frac{4}{12} \\ &= \frac{7}{12}\end{aligned}$$

2. Have students do **task 2, textbook p. 12**, either now or after the next activity.

3. Discuss multiplication and division of fractions when there are more than two terms.
   - Refer to **tasks 3-6, textbook p. 12**.
   - For task 3, remind students that 5 is $\frac{5}{1}$, and that when we multiply fractions, the numerator of the product is the product of the numerators of the terms, and the denominator of the product is the product of the denominators of the terms (i.e., we multiply the tops together and the bottom together.) We can simplify using any of the factors in the numerator with any of the factors in the denominator. You can show the steps as on the right, though students should be able to solve similarly to the illustration in the text.

     $$\begin{aligned}\frac{7}{9} \times 5 \times \frac{3}{8} &= \frac{7 \times 5 \times 3}{9 \times 8} \\ &= \frac{3 \times 7 \times 5}{3 \times 3 \times 8} \\ &= \frac{3}{3} \times \frac{7 \times 5}{3 \times 8} \\ &= 1 \times \frac{35}{24} \\ &= 1\frac{11}{24}\end{aligned}$$
   - For tasks 4-6, we change each division of a fraction to multiplication of its reciprocal, so all terms are multiplied together. Then we can solve by first reducing by any common factors.

- Side note: Tell students to always look for common factors before multiplying. This can greatly simplify the problem. Even with a division problem such as 2140 ÷ 16, we can simplify $\frac{2140}{16}$ by dividing the numerator and denominator by 2 four times, which can be done mentally, rather than doing the division problem $16\overline{)2140}$
- Optional: Tell students that as 4 ÷ 2 can be written as $\frac{4}{2}$, so can $4 \div \frac{1}{2}$ be written as a complex fraction, as shown here at the right. If they see a problem like that, they can simplify it by multiplying the numerator by the reciprocal of the denominator. (This complex fraction can be interpreted as "how many halves in 4".)

$$\frac{4}{\frac{1}{2}} = 4 \div \frac{1}{2} = 4 \times 2 = 8$$

4. Have students do **task 7, textbook p. 13**.

5. For more practice, have students do **problem 1, Practice 1B, textbook p. 15**.

Workbook Exercise 4

Activity 1.2b **Mixed operations with all four operations**

1. Discuss rules for order of operation when an expression has multiplication or division as well as addition or subtraction.
   - Discuss the contents of **p. 11 in the textbook**.
     - Here, we can see from the illustration that we are first finding $\frac{3}{4}$ times 4 to get 3, and then adding $\frac{1}{4}$ to get the sum $3\frac{1}{4}$. This follows order of operations (as in *Primary Mathematics 5A*, unit 1) where, if there is a calculation involving both addition and multiplication, we do the multiplication first. If we wanted to first add $\frac{1}{4}$ and $\frac{3}{4}$, and then multiply the sum by 4, we would have to use parentheses $(\frac{1}{4} + \frac{3}{4}) \times 4$. Whenever the equation does not indicate what operation should be done first, we know we have to do all the multiplication and division first.
   - Discuss tasks **8-9, textbook p. 13**, and tasks **11-12, textbook p. 14**.
     - Note that we first change all the division to multiplication.
     - Note that in some of these problems, calculations involving addition or subtraction are easier if the fraction is changed into a mixed number, rather than changing the whole number into an equivalent fraction, adding, and then converting the sum to a mixed number.
     - Remind students that their answer must always be in simplest form. You may require that all improper fractions be converted into a mixed number for the final answer.

#8. $4+\cancel{6}^{3}\times\frac{5}{\cancel{8}_{4}}=4+\frac{15}{4}=4+3\frac{3}{4}=7\frac{3}{4}$

#9. $1-\frac{4}{5}\div 6=1-\frac{\cancel{4}^{2}}{5}\times\frac{1}{\cancel{6}_{3}}=1-\frac{2}{15}=\frac{13}{15}$

#11. $\frac{3}{8}-\frac{\cancel{3}^{1}}{4}\times\frac{1}{\cancel{3}_{1}}=\frac{3}{8}-\frac{1}{4}=\frac{1}{8}$

#12. $\frac{5}{6}+\frac{2}{3}\div 4\times\frac{1}{2}=\frac{5}{6}+\frac{\cancel{2}^{1}}{3}\times\frac{1}{4}\times\frac{1}{\cancel{2}_{1}}=\frac{\cancel{5}^{10}}{\cancel{6}_{12}}+\frac{1}{12}=\frac{11}{12}$

2. Have students do **task 10, textbook p. 13**, and **task 13, textbook p. 14.**

3. For more practice, have students do **problem 2, Practice 1B, textbook p. 15.**

Workbook Exercise 5

Activity 1.2c **Mixed operations with parentheses**

1. Discuss **task 14, textbook p. 14.**
   Tell students that if the expression contains parentheses, we first find the value for the expression within the parentheses. The rules for order of operations are applied first to the expression in parentheses to replace it with a single term, and then to the entire expression.

$$\left(\frac{4}{5}-\frac{1}{2}\right)\div 4=\left(\frac{8}{10}-\frac{5}{10}\right)\div 4$$
$$=\frac{3}{10}\div 4$$
$$=\frac{3}{10}\times\frac{1}{4}$$
$$=\frac{3}{40}$$

2. Have students do **task 15, textbook p. 14.**

3. Have students do **problems 3-5, Practice 1B, textbook p. 15.**

Part 3: Word Problems — 4 sessions

Objectives

- Solve word problems which involve fractions.

Homework

- Workbook Exercise 7
- Workbook Exercise 8
- Workbook Exercise 6

Notes

Most of these problems can be solved by drawing bar models with units, and then finding the value of a unit, and using that to solve the problem. If there is a "before" situation and an "after" situation, they should both be diagrammed, taking care to show any relationships in the units between the two situations.

Students learned to draw bar models to solve fraction problems in earlier levels of *Primary Mathematics*.

Activity 1.3a **Word problems**

1. Discuss **textbook p. 16.**
   - Read the problem and the two questions farther down on the page. To answer the question, how much water is in the tank when it is $\frac{2}{3}$ full, we need to find what fraction of the tank 700 ml corresponds to. This calculation is shown in the thought bubble.
   - Once we find that $\frac{7}{15}$ of the total is 700 ml, we can find the amount of water for any other fraction of the total. Ask students to find the answer to the first question and then discuss the solutions. (The arrow can be read as "of the total".)
   - We could first find the value for $\frac{1}{15}$, then the value for the total capacity, then the value for $\frac{1}{5}$. Or, once we find the value for $\frac{1}{15}$, we can multiply to find the value for $\frac{3}{15}$, which is $\frac{1}{5}$.
   - We can also use division, and first find the total amount. 700 ml is $\frac{7}{15}$ of ?, or $700 \div \frac{7}{15} = ?$

$$\frac{7}{15} \longrightarrow 700 \text{ ml}$$
$$\frac{1}{15} \longrightarrow 700 \div 7 = 100 \text{ ml}$$
$$\frac{1}{5} = \frac{3}{15} \longrightarrow 100 \times 3 = 300 \text{ ml}$$
$$\frac{2}{3} = \frac{10}{15} \longrightarrow 100 \times 10 = 1000 \text{ ml}$$

700 ml is $\frac{7}{15}$ of what?

$700 \div \frac{7}{15} = 700 \times \frac{15}{7} = 1500$ ml

The tank holds 1500 ml.

$\frac{1}{5} \times 1500 \text{ ml} = 300 \text{ ml}$

$\frac{2}{3} \times 1500 \text{ ml} = 1000 \text{ ml}$

2. Discuss **task 1, textbook p. 17.**
   - Have students solve the problem and then discuss various solutions. He bought 84 chairs.
     - Once we find that $\frac{5}{12}$ of the chairs were yellow, we can use a bar diagram and solve the problem using units.

       Yellow chairs = 5 units = 35
       1 unit = 35 ÷ 5 = 7 chairs
       Total chairs = 12 units = 7 × 12 = 84

     - We can find the value for $\frac{1}{12}$ and then $\frac{12}{12}$.

$$\frac{5}{12} \longrightarrow 35$$
$$\frac{1}{12} \longrightarrow 35 \div 5 = 7$$
$$\frac{12}{12} \longrightarrow 7 \times 12 = 84$$

     - We can also solve the problem using division.

35 is $\frac{5}{12}$ of what?

$35 \div \frac{5}{12} = 35 \times \frac{12}{5} = 84$

3. Discuss **task 2, textbook p. 17.**

(b) Amount left = $\frac{3}{10}$ = \$90 3 units = \$90 1 unit = \$90 ÷ 3 = \$30 10 units = \$30 × 10 = \$300 He had \$300 at first.	or: $\frac{3}{10} \rightarrow \$90$ $\frac{10}{10} \rightarrow \$\frac{90}{3} \times 10 = \$300$	or: \$90 is $\frac{3}{10}$ of what? $\$90 \div \frac{3}{10} = \$90 \times \frac{10}{3} = \$300$

4. Have students work on some of the problems in **Practice 1C, textbook p. 20**, and share their solutions.

Workbook Exercise 7

Possible solutions:

#1. Remainder = $\frac{3}{5} \times 150 = 3 \times 30 = 90$ lb; Weight in each bag = 90 lb ÷ 5 = 18 lb of rice

#2. US stamps = 5 units
Canadian stamps = 3 units
Total stamps = 8 units = 400 stamps
Amount given to friend = 1 unit
Amount left = 7 units
8 units = 400
1 unit = 400 ÷ 8 = 50 stamps
7 units = 50 × 7 = 350 stamps

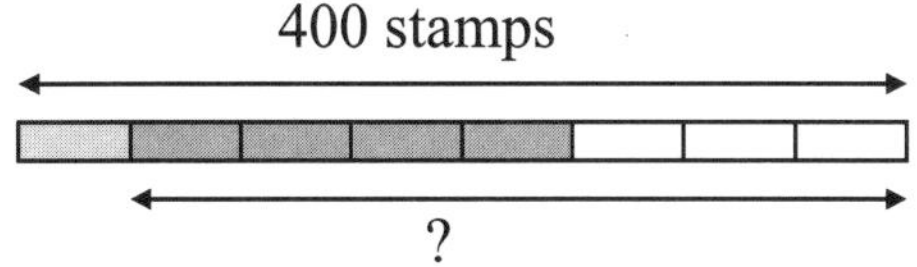

He had 350 stamps left.

OR: Fraction given to friend = $\frac{1}{5} \times \frac{5}{8} = \frac{1}{8}$

Fraction left = $\frac{7}{8}$; Amount left = $\frac{7}{8} \times 400 = 350$ stamps

#3. Total money = 7 units
Given to wife = 2 units
Remainder = 5 units
Amount spent = 3 units
Amount left = 2 units
2 units = \$300
1 unit = \$300 ÷ 2 = \$150
7 units = 7 × \$150 = \$1050

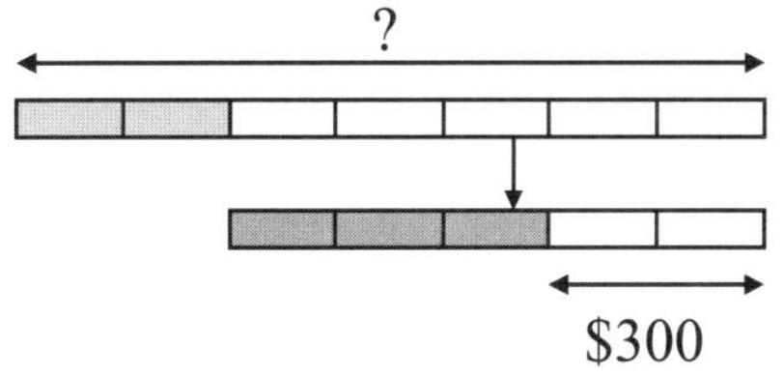

OR: Remainder = $\frac{5}{7}$; Fraction of remainder left = $\frac{2}{5} \times \frac{5}{7} = \frac{2}{7}$

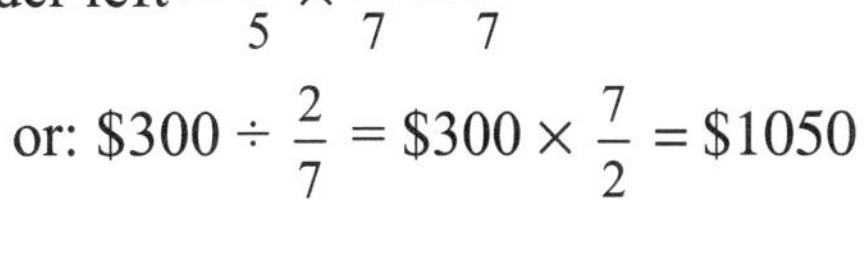

$\frac{2}{7} \rightarrow \$300$

$\frac{7}{7} \rightarrow \$\frac{300}{2} \times 7 = \$1050$

He had \$1050 at first.

or: $\$300 \div \frac{2}{7} = \$300 \times \frac{7}{2} = \$1050$

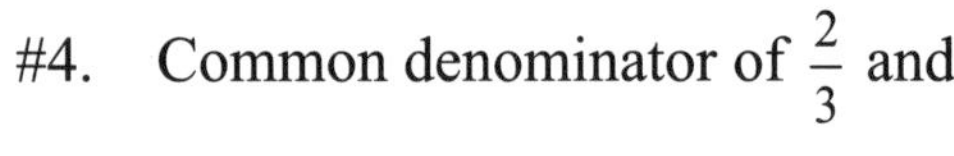

#4. Common denominator of $\frac{2}{3}$ and $\frac{1}{4}$ is 12. Draw bar with 12 units.

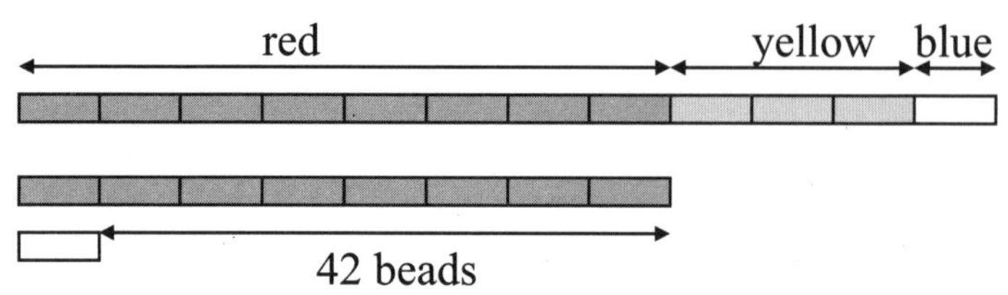

Red beads = 8 units
Yellow beads = 3 units
So, blue beads = 1 unit
7 units more red than blue beads
7 units = 42
12 units = $\frac{42}{7} \times 12 = 72$

There are 72 beads total.

or: Fraction blue beads
$= 1 - \frac{2}{3} - \frac{1}{4} = \frac{1}{12}$
Difference in red and blue beads
$= \frac{2}{3} - \frac{1}{12} = \frac{7}{12}$
$\frac{7}{12} \rightarrow 42,\ \frac{1}{12} \rightarrow 6,\ \frac{12}{12} \rightarrow 72$
or $42 \div \frac{7}{12} = 42 \times \frac{12}{7} = 72$ beads

---

Activity 1.3b — Word problems

1. Discuss **task 3, textbook p. 18.**
   - Lead students to see that the value of 3 white units (of the top bar's total of 5 units) is the same as the value of the 2 white units of the middle bar in the diagram.
     - The lowest common multiple of 3 and 2 is 6. So we can get equal units by dividing each unit of the top bar in half, and dividing each unit of the middle bar into thirds. Then the 3 white units of the top bar are now 6 smaller units, and the 2 units of the middle bar are also 6 smaller units.
     - The resulting total has 10 units, shown in the bottom bar, 4 units spent on the doll and 3 on the musical box.
     - 1 more unit was spent on the doll than on the music box. So 1 of these units is \$8. 3 units, the money she has left, is therefore \$24.

       1 unit = \$8.
       Money she had left = 3 units = $\$8 \times 3 = \$24$
   - We can also solve this by just using expressions with fractions, as shown at the right. But drawing bar diagrams still makes it easier to figure out how to solve such problem, even in other situations where it might not work out this neatly, with the remainder turning out to be 3 times the difference.

     Remainder = $1 - \frac{2}{5} = \frac{3}{5}$

     Fraction spent on doll = $\frac{1}{2} \times \frac{3}{5} = \frac{3}{10}$

     Difference = $\frac{2}{5} - \frac{3}{10} = \frac{1}{10} \rightarrow \$8$

     Total money = $\$8 \div \frac{1}{10} = \$80$

     Fraction of money left = $1 - \frac{4}{10} - \frac{3}{10} = \frac{3}{10}$

     Amount left $\frac{3}{10} \times \$80 = \$24$

2. Discuss **task 4, textbook p. 18.**
   - Lead students to see that half of the book is half way through one of the fifth units, so we change to tenth units. There were 120 pages in the book.
   - We can also solve this problem by using expressions with fractions: Even so, drawing the picture helps us come up with the right expression.

     Fraction of the book she read on Tuesday $= \frac{1}{2} - \frac{2}{5} = \frac{5}{10} - \frac{4}{10} = \frac{1}{10}$

     12 is $\frac{1}{10}$ of the total pages; total number of pages $= 12 \div \frac{1}{10} = 12 \times 10 = 120$

3. Discuss **task 5, textbook p. 19.**
   - Even though the dotted line in the diagram looks to be about half of a fourth unit it is not, and we do not know exactly what fraction of the total is 24 beads when the bar diagram is drawn.

4. Discuss **task 6, textbook p. 19.**
   - Lead students through the problem as it is worked out in the textbook.
   - 10 jugs = $\frac{5}{8}$ bucket, so $\frac{1}{8}$ bucket = $\frac{10}{5}$ jugs = 2 jugs. 4 jugs is therefore $\frac{2}{8}$ of a bucket. We are told that $\frac{3}{8}$ of the total is 4 jugs 5 cups, so $\frac{1}{8}$ must be 5 cups. Label two of the white units as 4 jugs to illustrate this.

5. Have students work on some of the problems 1-7 in **Practice 1C, textbook p. 20**, and share their solutions.

Workbook Exercise 8
Possible solutions:

#1. Students should label the diagram.

After buying the handbag, she has $\frac{2}{5}$ of her money left. At first, the bar is divided into fifths. Since the handbag costs twice as much as the dress, the dress cost half as much as the handbag, or $1\frac{1}{2}$ of the fifths. Divide the fifths in half to have 6 units for the handbag. There are 4 units left for the dress and belt. The dress costs 3 units, and 1 unit is left for the belt. The dress is 2 units more than the belt. So 2 units is \$20. 2 units is the same as $\frac{1}{5}$ of her money.

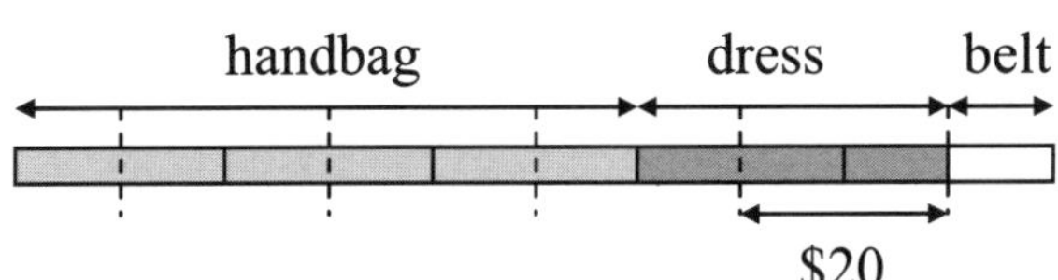

Total money = $\$20 \times 5 = \$100$

#2. Students should label the diagram as they work through the problem.

The diagram shows \$48 is $\frac{1}{4}$ of his money, but we do not know that at first. If we divide the remainder into thirds, and then mark $\frac{2}{3}$ of the remainder as $\frac{1}{2}$ of his money, then we can see that one of those units is $\frac{1}{4}$ of his money. So the amount spent on the watch has to be $\frac{1}{4}$ of his money.

All his money = \$48 × 4 = \$192

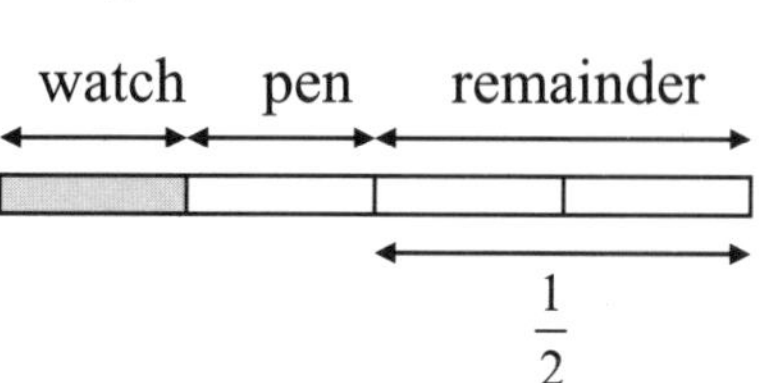

Activity 1.3c **Practice**

1. Have students do the rest of the problems in **Practice 1C, textbook p. 20** and problems from **Practice 1D, textbook p. 21** and share their solutions. This can take more than one session. Possible solutions to selected problems are given below. Students may have alternate solutions.

Practice 1C

#8. 8 units = 480
1 unit = 480 ÷ 8 = 60
2 units = 60 × 2 = 120

or: Fraction that are foreign = $\frac{3}{8}$.

Fraction more U.S. than foreign = $\frac{5}{8} - \frac{3}{8} = \frac{1}{4}$

$\frac{1}{4} \times 480 = 120$

He has 120 more foreign stamps than U.S. stamps.

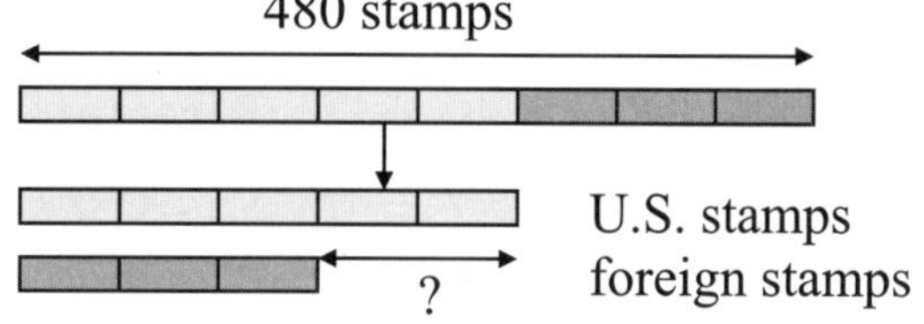

#9. Divide a bar into thirds. Flour for cookies is $\frac{1}{3}$ of the total, and the remainder is two thirds. One fourth of the remainder is one half of one of the thirds. So divide each unit into half to give 6 units.
6 units = 24
3 units = 24 ÷ 2= 12

or: Remainder = $\frac{2}{3}$. Fraction of remainder not used = $\frac{3}{4}$

Fraction left = $\frac{3}{4} \times \frac{2}{3} = \frac{1}{2}$ $\frac{1}{2} \times 24 = 12$

12 lb of flour was left.

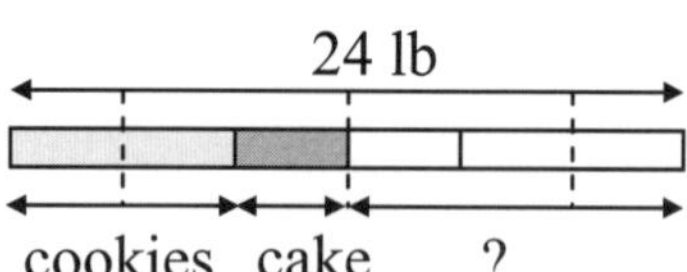

Practice 1D

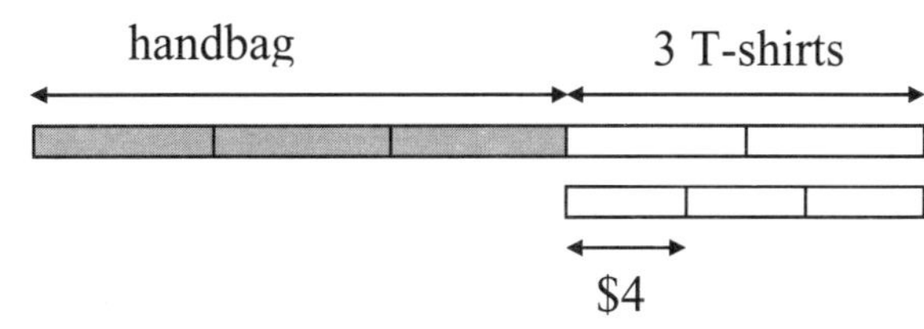

#3. 2 units = $3 \times \$4 = \$12$

3 units = $\$\frac{12}{2} \times 3 = \$18$

The handbag cost $18.

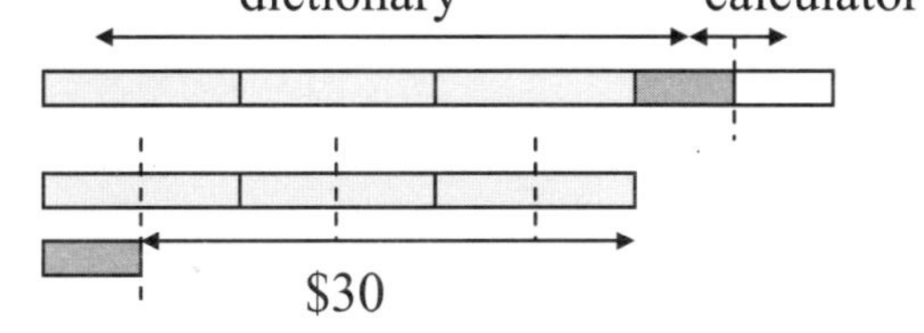

#4. Divide a bar up into fourths. The remainder is one fourth. Since she spent half the remainder on the calculator, divide each fourth into two units. The dictionary is 5 units more than the calculator.

5 units = $30

6 units = $\$\frac{30}{5} \times 6 = \$36$

The dictionary cost $36.

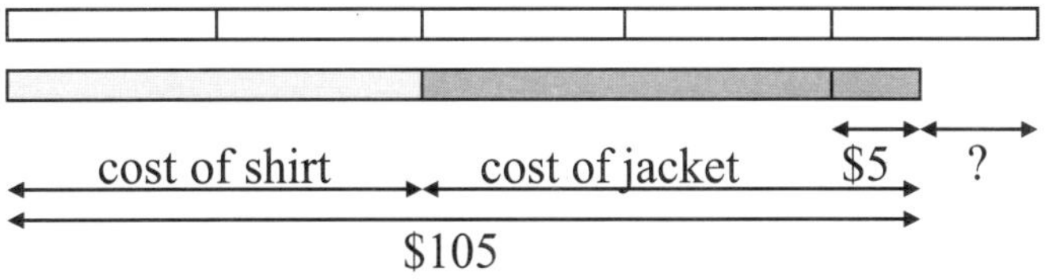

#7. Divide his money into 5 units.
The shirt costs 2 units.
The jacket costs $5 more than 2 units. Total spent is 4 units plus the $5.

4 units = $105 – $5 = $100

1 unit = $100 ÷ 4 = $25

Amount left = 1 unit – $5 = $25 – $5 = $20

#8.

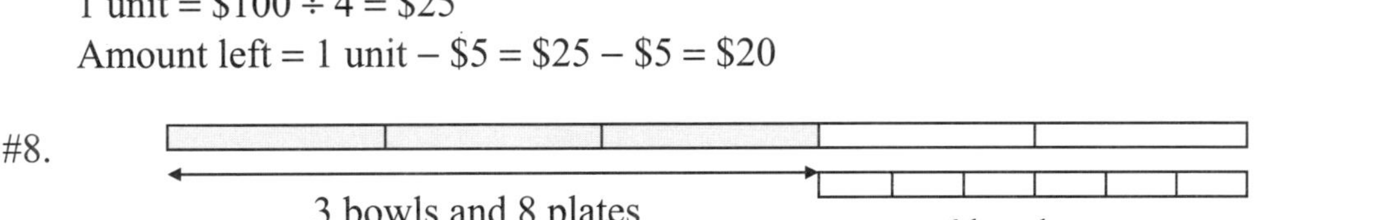

Divide bar into fifths. 2 units are left, and she can buy 6 bowls with 2 units.
So she could buy 3 bowls with 1 unit of money.

1 unit = cost of 3 bowls

3 units = cost of 3 bowls and 8 plates

So, 2 units = cost of 8 plates

and 1 unit = cost of 4 plates

5 units = $4 \times 5 = 20$ plates

She could buy 20 plates.

Circles

Objectives

- Identify the center, diameter, and radius of a circle.
- Measure the radius or diameter of a circle.
- Construct a circle for a given diameter or radius.
- Relate the circumference of a circle to its diameter.
- Relate the area of a circle to its radius.
- Determine the circumference or area of a circle when given its diameter or radius.
- Determine the perimeter and area of semicircles and quarter circles and related figures.
- Determine the perimeter and area of composite figures formed from squares, rectangles, triangles, semicircles and quarter circles.

Suggested number of sessions: 11

	Objectives	Textbook	Workbook	Activities
Part 1 : Radius and Diameter				**2 sessions**
14	▪ Identify the center, diameter, and radius of a circle. ▪ Measure the radius or diameter of a circle.	^{US}p. 22 ^{US}pp. 23-24, tasks 1-2 ^{3d}p. 6 ^{3d}pp. 7-8, tasks 1-2		2.1a
15	▪ Construct circles of a given radius or diameter. ▪ Find the diameter when given the radius, or vice versa.	^{US}pp. 24-25, tasks 3-7 ^{3d}pp. 8-9, tasks 3-7	^{US}Ex. 9 ^{3d}Ex. 1	2.1b
Part 2 : Circumference				**4 sessions**
16	▪ Relate the circumference of a circle to its diameter.	^{US}p. 26 ^{US}p 27, task 1 ^{3d}p. 10 ^{3d}p. 11, task 1		2.2a
17	▪ Find the circumference of a circle when given its diameter or radius.	^{US}pp. 27-29, tasks 2-8 ^{3d}pp. 11-12, tasks 2-8	^{US}Ex. 10 ^{3d}Ex. 2	2.2b
18	▪ Find the perimeter of a semicircle or quarter circle and related figures. ▪ Find the perimeter of a compound shape made up of squares, rectangles, triangles, semicircles and/ or quarter circles.	^{US}p. 29, tasks 9-11 ^{3d}p. 13, tasks 9-11	^{US}Ex. 11 ^{3d}Ex. 3	2.2c
19	▪ Practice.	^{US}p. 30, Practice 2A ^{38}p. 14, Practice 1A		2.2d

	Objectives	Textbook	Workbook	Activities
Part 3 : Area				**5 sessions**
20	▪ Relate the area of a circle to its radius.	US p. 31 US p. 32, task 1 3d p. 15 3d p. 16, task 1		2.3a
21	▪ Find the area of a circle when given its diameter or radius.	US pp. 33-34, tasks 1-7 3d pp. 17-18, tasks 1-7	US Ex. 12 3d Ex. 4	2.3b
22	▪ Find the area of a semicircle or quarter circle and related figures.	US pp. 34-35, tasks 8-10 US p. 36, Practice 2B 3d pp. 18-19, tasks 8-10 3d p. 20, Practice 1B	US Ex. 13 US Ex. 14 3d Ex. 5 3d Ex. 6	2.3c
23	▪ Find the area of a compound shape made up of squares, rectangles, triangles, semicircles and/ or quarter circles.	US p. 35, tasks 11-12 US p. 37, Practice 2C 3d p. 19, tasks 11-12 3d p. 21, Practice 1C	US Ex. 15 3d Ex. 7	2.3d
24	▪ Practice.		US Ex. 16 3d Ex. 8	2.3e

Part 1: Radius and Diameter — 2 sessions

Objectives

- Identify the center, diameter, and radius of a circle.
- Measure the radius or diameter of a circle.
- Construct circles of a given radius or diameter.
- Find the diameter when the radius is given.
- Find the radius when the diameter is given.

Materials

- Compasses
- Rulers (centimeters)
- String and pins
- Paper circles of various diameters

Homework

US edition	**3rd edition**
• Workbook Exercise 9	Workbook Exercise 1

Notes

In earlier levels of *Primary Mathematic*, students learned how to find the perimeter of rectilinear shapes, and the area of triangles and of rectangles. In this unit they will learn to find the circumference (perimeter) and area of circles, semicircles, and quarter circles, as well as the area or perimeter of composite figures which include circles, semicircles, and quarter circles.

In this part, they will learn to find the center, radius, and diameter of a circle.

A circle is a set of points all of which are the same distance from a given point, the center. The center is usually labeled with the letter "O" here.

A radius is any line segment from the center of the circle to a point on the circle. A circle has an infinite number of radii (plural for radius), all the same length. The term *radius* is also used to mean the *length* of the radius.

A diameter is a line segment that has its endpoints on the circle and passes through the center of the circle. The term diameter is also used to mean the length of the diameter.

Students will not learn a formal definition for radius or diameter at this time, but will learn to recognize and measure the radius and diameter of a circle.

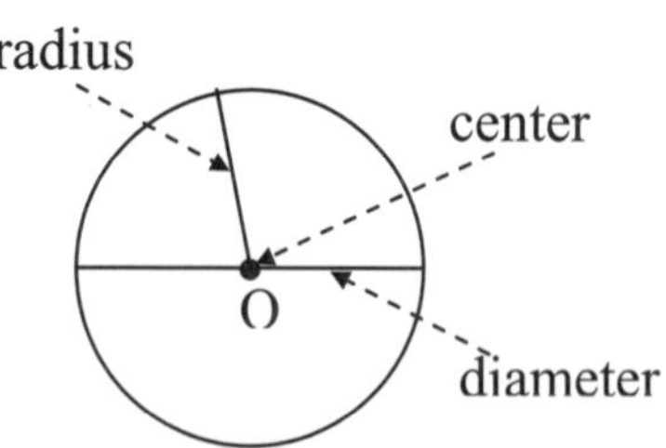

The diameter of a circle is twice its radius.
Diameter = Radius × 2
Radius = Diameter ÷ 2

Activity 2.1a **Circle, radius, and diameter**

1. Define *circle*, practice using a compass.
   - Students can do this activity in groups. This activity is optional; but it does give students a good "feel" for a circle as a set of points the same distance from a given point.
     - Provide each group with a cardboard sheet, a piece of paper, a tack, string, and a pencil.
     - Student must stick the tack through the paper and into the cardboard, about in the middle. They tie the string in a loop such that the doubled length is less than the distance from the tack to the edge of the paper. Then they loop the string around the tack and the pencil. They can draw a circle by keeping the string tight and trying to draw a straight line. The string pulls the pencil around in a circle.
     - Point out that the distance from the tack to the curved line (circle) is always the same.

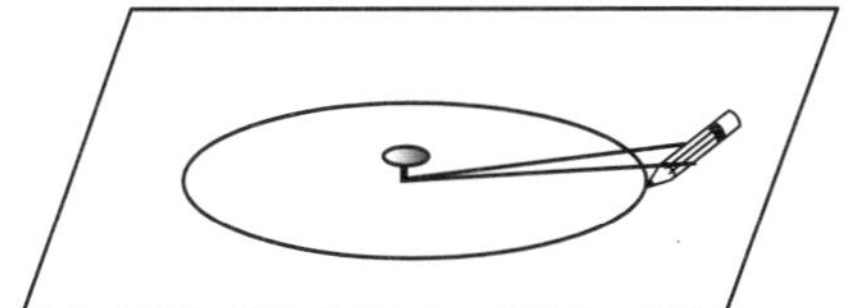

   - Show students how to use a compass and have them practice drawing circles with the compass.

2. Define diameter and radius.
   - Refer to **p. 22 in the textbook [3rd p. 6]**. Draw a similar circle on the board. Use a meter stick or yardstick to draw the diameter MP.
   - Ask students to describe the line segment MP. It intersects with the circle and passes through the center. Tell students that this line is called a *diameter* of the circle. Call on a student to draw a second diameter, using the ruler.

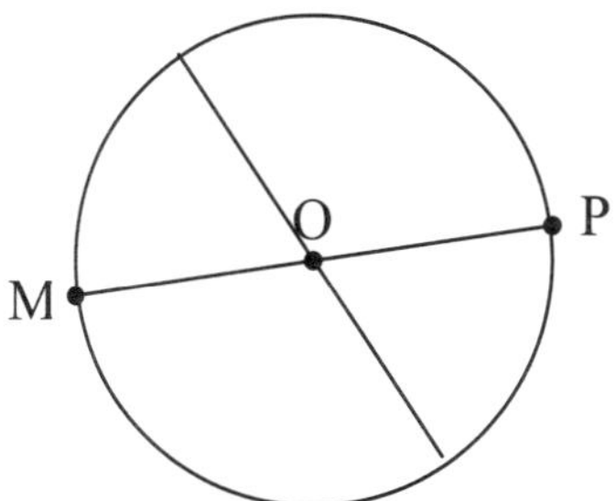

   - Tell students that the length of this new line is also called the diameter of the circle. Since all points on the circle are the same distance from the center, any diameter line can be used to measure the diameter of the circle. The length of all the diameter lines is the same. So if the word "diameter" is being used to mean the line segment that passes through the center and intersects the circle, then we can say there are many possible diameters. However, if we are using the word to mean the length of the diameter (e.g., "The diameter of the circle is 10 cm."), then "diameter" means that particular length only.
   - Ask students to describe the line segment OP. The line goes from the center of the circle to the edge. Tell student that this is called a radius of the circle. OM is also a *radius* of the circle. Ask students if OM = OP. It does. Both are radii of the circle (radii is the plural of radius)
   - The length of a radius line is also called the radius of the circle.
   - Draw a circle with various line segments, including one radius and one diameter. Ask students to identify the center, radius, and diameter of the circle.

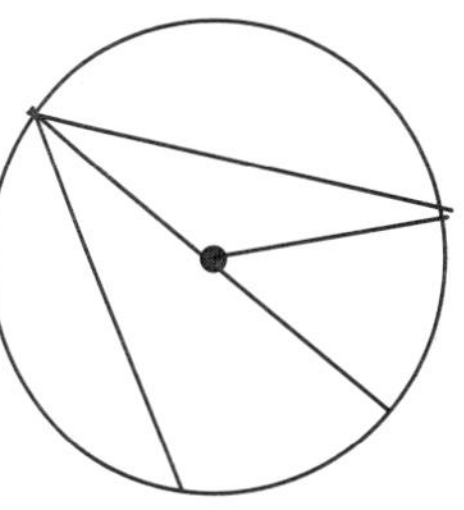

3. Have students do **tasks 1-2, textbook pp. 23-24 [3rd pp. 7-8]**.
   - You can also have them measure the radii and diameters of some circles that they draw with a compass.

Activity 2.1b **Radius and diameter**

1. Compare radius and diameter.
   - Have students draw a circle on paper with a compass, cut the circle out, and fold, as shown in **task 3, textbook p. 24 [3rd p. 8]**. It is obvious from this that the diameter is twice the radius.

2. Draw circles of a given radius or diameter.
   - Have students do **tasks 4-5, textbook p. 25 [3rd p. 9]**. Note that compasses can be set for a specific radius, so if they are given a diameter, they need to halve it.
   - US: Have students draw circles of a given diameter in inches.

3. Have students do **tasks 6-7, textbook p. 25 [3rd p. 9]**.

Workbook Exercise 9 [3rd Exercise 1]

Part 2: Circumference — 4 sessions

Objectives

- Relate the circumference of a circle to its diameter.
- Find the circumference of a circle when given its diameter or radius.
- Find the perimeter of a semicircle and quarter circle and related shapes.
- Find the perimeter of a compound shape made up of rectangles, triangles, semicircles, and/or quarter circles.

Materials

- Cardboard circles of various diameters, or cans or other cylindrical objects
- Compasses, rulers

Homework

US edition	3rd edition
• Workbook Exercise 10	Workbook Exercise 2
• Workbook Exercise 11	Workbook Exercise 3

Notes

The ratio of the circumference of a circle to its diameter is a constant; that is, it is always the same for every circle. Mathematicians have found that it is impossible to find the exact value of the quotient $\frac{\text{circumference}}{\text{diameter}}$ as a ratio of two whole numbers. They use the Greek letter π (which is sometimes written as "pi" and is pronounced like "pie") to represent this quotient. Some calculators give the approximate value of 3.141592654. In this book, 3.14, 3.142, or $\frac{22}{7}$ are used as an approximation for the value of π. (These approximations have been used historically in the building trade, in engineering, in astronomy, and in school books.)

In the text, the formula for the circumference of a circle is given as
Circumference = π × Diameter.

This is a good place for students to learn to use letters to stand for names in a formula. If we use C for circumference, and d for diameter, we can write this as $\boldsymbol{C = \pi d}$

The formula for circumference is often given as $\boldsymbol{C = 2\pi r}$, where r is the radius.

Students should know both of these formulas.

You can use P to stand for Perimeter.

Note: The detailed explanation that follows is not meant for general class instruction, unless some students question you on this topic.

A number that can be expressed as a fraction is a rational number. A number that cannot be expressed as a fraction is an irrational number (not a crazy number, just not a ratio). All fractions can be written as a decimal which either terminates, such as $\frac{1}{2} = 0.5$, or as a non-ending decimal that repeats a pattern, such as $\frac{1}{6} = 0.1666\ldots$ or $\frac{1}{7} = 0.142857142\ldots$ Only fractions which, in their simplest form, have a denominator that has only 2's and 5's as its factors can be written as a finite terminating decimal. All other fractions have non-ending repeating decimals.

To convert a fraction, $\frac{a}{b}$ into a decimal, we calculate a ÷ b by long division. At each step of the long division, the remainder, r, is a whole number between 0 and one less than b, that is, $0 \leq r < b$. If the remainder is 0, the decimal terminates. If it is never 0, no matter how long one continues to divide, then the decimal is called a repeating decimal. For example, in calculating $1 \div 7$ for $\frac{1}{7}$, the remainders are, in order, 3, 2, 6, 4, 5, 1 … Each is greater than 0 and less than 7. Since there are only 6 possibilities, one of them will repeat by the seventh step at the latest. The seventh remainder is 3, and the pattern repeats itself. When the remainder occurs twice, from then on the calculation will repeat, so the decimal will repeat, 0.142857142…. In $\frac{1}{3}$ the remainder repeats by the second step, and further division continues to give a remainder of 1. In $\frac{1}{6} = 0.1666\ldots$ the remainder repeats at the third step and further division continues to give a remainder of 4. In $\frac{1}{17}$, the remainder does not repeat until the 17th step!

A terminating decimal can easily be converted into a fraction: $0.345 = \frac{345}{1000} = \frac{69}{500}$. A repeating decimal can also be converted into a fraction by multiplying it by two different powers of 10 and subtracting, choosing the powers of 10 to align with the repeating part so that the subtraction gets rid of the decimal part.

Let $x = 0.1666\ldots$ We want to find x.

$$\begin{aligned} 100x &= 16.666\ldots \\ -\ 10x &= 01.666\ldots \\ \hline 90x &= 15 \\ x &= \frac{15}{90} = \frac{1}{6} \end{aligned}$$

Let $x = 0.454545\ldots$ We want to find x.

$$\begin{aligned} 100x &= 45.4545 \\ -\ x &= 0.4545 \\ \hline 99x &= 45 \\ x &= \frac{45}{99} = \frac{5}{11} \end{aligned}$$

A non-terminating and non-repeating decimal cannot be written as a fraction. π is an irrational number, even though it is defined as the "ratio" of the circumference to the diameter of a circle. A rational number that can be expressed as a fraction has to be able to be written with a whole number in both the numerator and the denominator. It is not possible to have a whole number for the diameter of a circle and get a whole number for its circumference.

Activity 2.2a

π

1. Explore circumference of a circle.
   - Tell students that the boundary line of a circle is called its circumference. That is, the perimeter of a circle is its circumference. You may want to tell students that "circum–" is a Latin prefix meaning "around" and "–ferre" means "to carry".
   - Have students do the activity in the **textbook on p. 26 [3rd p. 10]**. Since it is difficult to measure the circumference of a paper or drawn circle accurately with string, this activity will work better if you provide students with cylinders of various diameters to use to both draw their circles and put their strings around. You can use cardboard circles, the bottom of flower pots or tin cans, a round base on a lamp-stand, jar lids, etc. Use a variety of sizes, so that students can confirm that regardless of the size of the circle, the circumference is slightly more than 3 times the diameter.
   - Have students measure the circumference and diameter of their circles, and put their results in a chart, as in **task 1, textbook p. 27 [3rd p. 11]**. Add a column to the chart to put the value for circumference ÷ diameter. This ratio should come close to 3.14
   - Tell students that mathematicians have come up with various methods of finding the ratio of circumference to diameter that depend on mathematical properties rather than just measurement, and have found that this ratio is an unending decimal, 3.14159265358979323846264...
   - Tell students that all fractions can be written as a decimal which either terminates, such as $\frac{1}{2} = 0.5$, or as a non-ending decimal that repeats a pattern, such as $\frac{1}{3} = 0.3333\ldots$ or $\frac{1}{7} = 0.14285714285\ldots.$ Conversely, any decimal that terminates or has a repeating pattern can be written as a fraction.
   - Mathematicians tried for years to find a repeating pattern for the decimals after 3 for the ratio of the circumference of a circle to its diameter, and in 1768 Johann Lambert proved that there *cannot* be any such repeating pattern. So this ratio cannot be written as a fraction.
   - Rather than write out this ratio, we use the Greek letter π (pronounced "pie") to stand for the ratio of the circumference to the diameter of a circle. It is sometimes written as "pi".

2. Discuss the formula for the circumference of a circle.
   - Refer to the boxed words in the middle of **textbook p. 27 [3rd p. 11]**. Discuss the following:
   - If $\frac{\text{circumference}}{\text{diameter}} = \pi$, then circumference = π × diameter. So if we know the diameter of a circle, we can calculate the circumference, using π.
   - Because π is an unending, non-repeating decimal, we have to use an approximation for π in computations involving π. We will use the approximations 3.14 or $\frac{22}{7}$ (which equals 3.142857142857….)
   - Rewrite the formula given here as $C = \pi d$. Tell your student that C stands for circumference and d for the length of the diameter. This is a mathematical formula, where the letters stand for specific measurements, and relates C to d. For any value of d, there is only one value for C. Emphasize that since we can only approximate π, C will be an approximation too.

$C = \pi d$

- Ask students for a formula for the circumference using the radius instead of the diameter. Since the diameter is twice the radius, we can write this as $d = 2r$. So $C = \pi 2r$. Tell students that even though π is a constant, that is, only one value can be assigned to it (even though we use approximations), we still write it after the whole number in formulas like this. $C = 2\pi r$

$C = 2\pi r$

3. Have students use 3.14 for π and calculate the circumference of the circles used previously to see how close they come to their measured values.

Activity 2.2b **Circumference**

1. Discuss **tasks 2-4, textbook pp. 27-28 [3rd pp. 11-12]**.
   - Note that these problems are written so that, if we are told to use $\pi = \frac{22}{7}$, then the diameter is usually a multiple of 7, and we should simplify the fraction. For example, in task 4,
     $C = \frac{22}{7} \times 28 = \frac{22}{\cancel{7}_1} \times \cancel{28}^4 = 88 \text{ cm}$

2. Have students do **tasks 5-8, textbook pp. 28-29 [3rd pp. 12-13]**.

3. Write the problem shown here on the board and have students solve it.
   The bicycle goes a distance of 1 circumference of a tire in 1 revolution. So in 100 revolutions it goes the distance:
   $\frac{22}{\cancel{7}_1} \times \cancel{56}^8 \times 100 = 17600 \text{ cm} = 176 \text{ m}$

A bicycle tire has a diameter of 56 cm. How far does it go in 100 revolutions?

Workbook Exercise 10 [3rd Exercise 2]

Activity 2.2c **Perimeter**

1. Find the perimeter of semicircles and quarter circles.
   - Draw a semicircle, label the diameter as 14 cm or some convenient multiple of 7.
     - Ask students to find the perimeter, taking $\pi = \frac{22}{7}$.
     - The perimeter is half the circumference plus the straight side. (A common error in these kinds of problems is to concentrate on finding the length of the curved boundary, and then forget to add in the length of the straight side.)

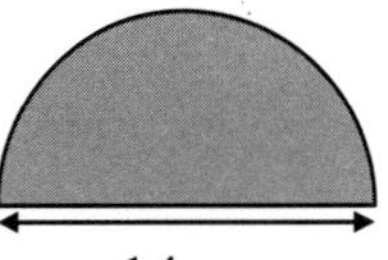

14 cm

$$P = \left(\frac{1}{2} \times \pi \times \text{diameter}\right) + 14$$
$$= \left(\frac{1}{\cancel{2}_1} \times \frac{22}{\cancel{7}_1} \times \cancel{14}^{\cancel{2}^1}\right) + 14$$
$$= 22 + 14$$
$$= 36 \text{ cm}$$

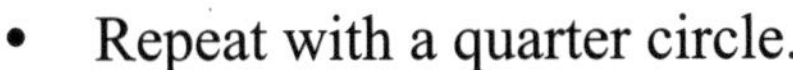

   - Repeat with a quarter circle.
     - Tell students that a quarter circle is also called a quadrant.

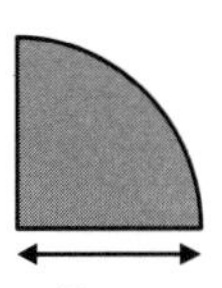

7 cm

$$P = \left(\frac{1}{4} \times \pi \times 2 \times \text{radius}\right) + 7 + 7$$
$$= \left(\frac{1}{\cancel{4}_1} \times \frac{\cancel{22}^{11}}{\cancel{7}_1} \times \cancel{2}^1 \times \cancel{7}^1\right) + 7 + 7$$
$$= 11 + 7 + 7$$
$$= 25 \text{ cm}$$

2. Discuss **tasks 9-11, textbook p. 29 [3rd p. 13]**.
   - Note that task 10 asks for the length of the wire in terms of π. This can be confusing to students. Tell students that this means they can leave the answer as the product of two factors, some number and π, and do not have to do the final multiplication by π. They have to do all the other operations.

     #10. Length $= 3 \times \frac{1}{2}$ of the circumference of a circle with diameter 10 cm

     $= 3 \times \frac{1}{2} \times \pi \times 10 = 15 \times \pi = 15\pi$ cm

   - For task 11, elicit solutions from students. Lead them to see that we do not have to find two half circumferences and then add them together as well as adding the two sides of the rectangular part. We can simply find the circumference of a whole circle.

     #11. The two semicircles make a whole circle.

     Perimeter = (circumference of the circle) + (length of the two sides of the rectangle)

     $= (\frac{22}{7} \times 14) + (2 \times 30) = 44 + 60 = 104$ cm

3. Optional: Have students find the perimeters of the shaded portion of figures A-D on p. 43 of this guide. Answers are on p. 44.

Workbook Exercise 11 [3rd Exercise 3]

Activity 2.2d **Practice**

1. Have students do **Practice 2A, textbook p. 30 [3rd Practice 1A, p. 14]** and share their solutions.

   #6. The perimeter is the circumference of the larger semicircle plus the circumference of the two smaller semicircles. The two smaller semicircles together make a whole circle.

   $$P = (\frac{1}{2} \times \pi \times 20) + (\pi \times 10) = (10 \times \pi) + (10 \times \pi) = 20\pi \text{ cm}$$

   Notice that the perimeter of the larger semicircle is the same as the sum of the perimeters of the two small semicircles.

Part 3: Area — 6 sessions

Objectives

- Relate the area of a circle to its radius.
- Find the area of a circle when given its diameter.
- Find the area of a semicircle or quarter circle.
- Find the area of compound figures made up of semicircles and quarter circles.
- Find the area of a compound figure made up of rectangles, triangles, semicircles, and/or quarter circles.

Materials

- Compasses, rulers
- Paper circles with various diameters
- Paper circle divided into 24 equal parts (see p. 39 of this guide)
- Centimeter graph paper (see p. 38 of this guide)

Homework

US edition	3rd edition
• Workbook Exercise 12	Workbook Exercise 4
• Workbook Exercise 13	Workbook Exercise 5
• Workbook Exercise 14	Workbook Exercise 6
• Workbook Exercise 15	Workbook Exercise 7
• Workbook Exercise 16	Workbook Exercise 8

Notes

The formula that is commonly used for the area of a circle is

$$A = \pi r^2$$

Where A is area and r is the radius.

A common error to watch out for is using the diameter rather than the radius in this formula when the diameter, instead of the radius, is given in the problem.

Centimeter Graph Paper

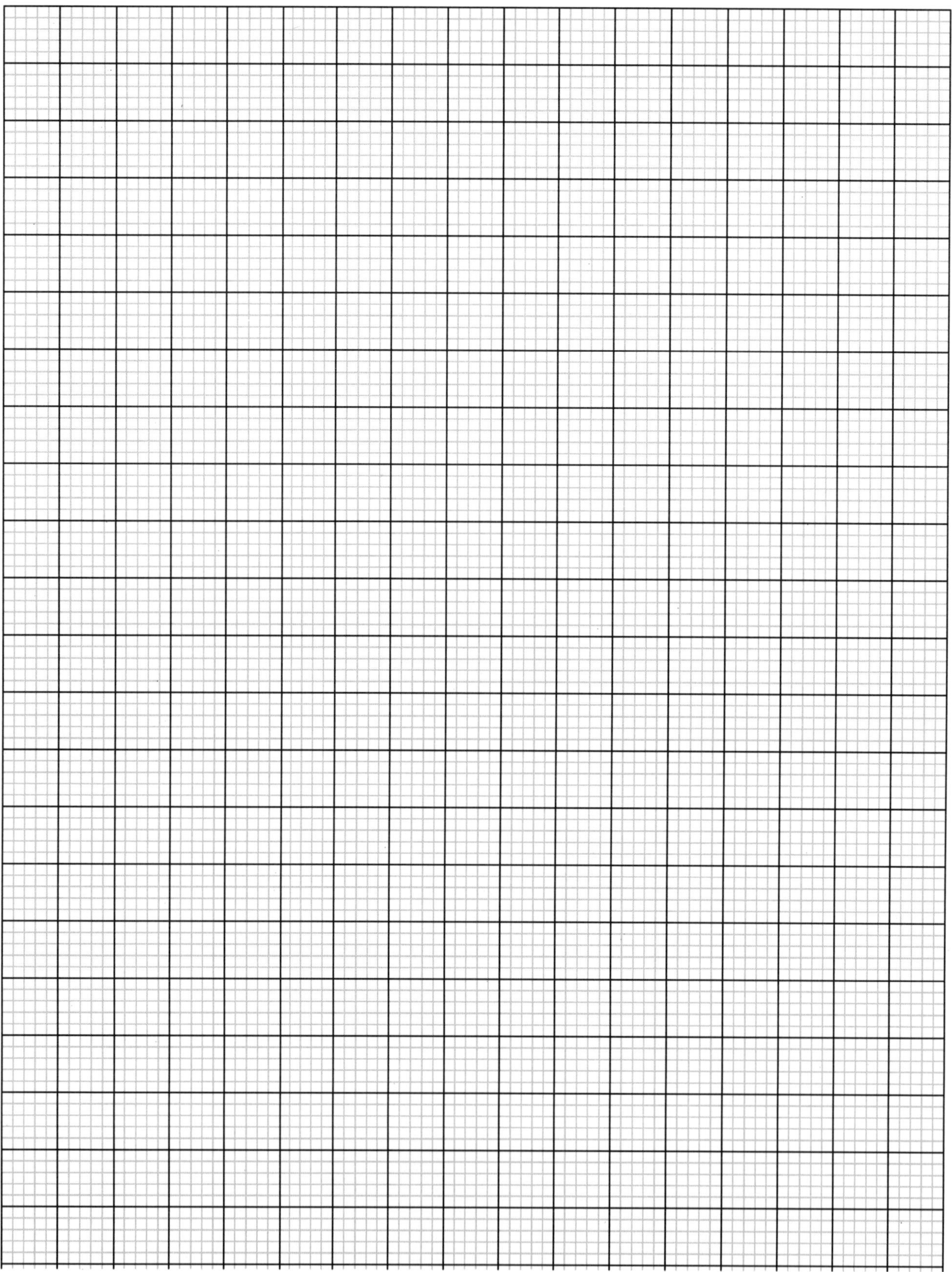

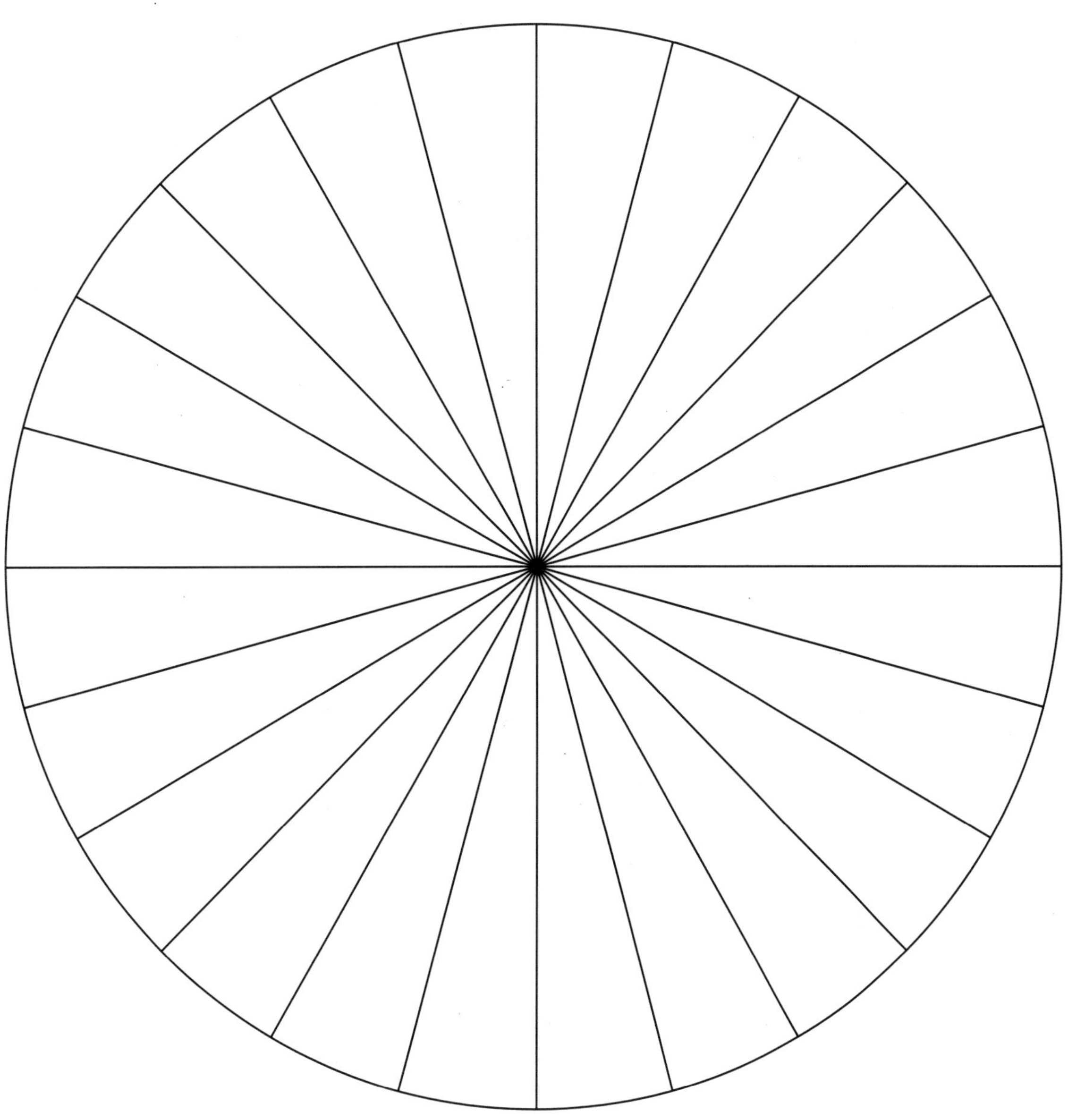

Activity 2.3a **Area of a circle**

1. Explore the area of a circle.
   - Refer to **textbook p. 31 [3rd p. 15]**.
     - Have students find the estimated area of a quarter of the circle by counting the shaded squares. (Where at least half of the square is inside the quarter circle, the whole square is shaded.) Then they multiply this figure by 4 to get the approximate area of one whole circle.
     - Provide students with centimeter graph paper and compasses. Have students draw circles of various diameters (maximum 18 cm), shade a quarter of the circle, and find the estimated area by counting squares.
     - Have them write the radii and total area of their circles on a chart on the board.
     - Have students look at their circles or p. 31 (3rd p. 15) in the textbook. Have them draw 4 squares corresponding to the quarter circles of the circle. The area of each square is the radius squared. The area of each quarter circle is a little more than $\frac{3}{4}$ of the square. So the area of the entire circle is a little more than $4 \times \frac{3}{4} = 3$ times the area of a square with a side the length of the radius.
     - Remind students that the circumference of a circle is slightly more than 3 times the diameter, or about 3.14 times the diameter.
     - Divide each area by 3.14. The result is approximately the square of the radius.
     - So, the area of a circle is about $3.14 \times$ radius $\times$ radius.
   - Refer to **textbook p. 32 [3rd p. 16]**.
     - If time permits, have students do this activity. You can use the circle on p. 39 of this guide.
     - The figure formed is almost a rectangle. The area of this rectangle will be the same as the area of the circle. Lead students to see that as the sections get smaller; the side for the figure's length will get closer to a straight line. The length of this rectangle, then, approaches half the circumference of the circle as the sections get smaller. The width of the rectangle is the radius of the circle.
     - Using r for radius, the length of the rectangle is $\frac{1}{2} \times 2 \times \pi \times r$ and its width is r. The area of the rectangle is length $\times$ width.

       Area of the rectangle $= (\frac{1}{2} \times 2 \times \pi \times r) \times r = \pi \times r \times r$.
   - Remind students (from *Primary Mathematics 6A*) that we can write $r \times r$ as r^2. So we can write the formula for the area of a circle as

     $A = \pi r^2$, where A is the Area and r is the radius
   - Have students find the areas of the circles they drew for the first activity using this formula, and taking $\pi = 3.14$.

Activity 2.3b **Area**

1. Find the area of a circles when given its radius or diameter.
   - Discuss **tasks 2-7, textbook pp. 33-34 [3rd pp. 17-18]**.
   - Have students check that their answer is reasonable by finding an estimated answer, using $\pi = 3$. Examples for estimated answers are given here for tasks 4, 5, 6(a), and 6(b).

#4. $A = \frac{22}{7} \times 7 \times 7 = 154 \text{ m}^2$

Estimation: $3 \times 7 \times 7 = 3 \times 49 \approx 3 \times 50 = 150$

#5. $A = 3.14 \times 6 \times 6 = 113.04 \text{ m}^2$

Estimation: $3 \times 6 \times 6 = 3 \times 36 \approx 3 \times 40 = 120$

#6. (a) $\frac{22}{7} \times 14 \times 14 = 616 \text{ cm}^2$

Estimation: $3 \times 10 \times 20 = 600$ (Rounding one up and one down will give a closer estimation.)

(b) $\frac{22}{7} \times 21 \times 21 = 1386 \text{ cm}^2$

Estimation: $3 \times 20 \times 20 = 1200$

Workbook Exercise 12 [3rd Exercise 4]

Activity 2.3c **Area of semicircles and quarter-circles**

1. Discuss **tasks 8-10, textbook pp. 34-35 [3rd pp. 18-19]**.
   - For task 10, the shaded areas consist of 4 quarter circles, which together make one whole circle. So the area is the area of a whole circle.
   - You can ask students to also find the perimeter of these figures.

2. Have students do **problems 1-7, Practice 2B, textbook p. 36 [3rd Practice 1B p. 20]**.
   - You can also ask students to find the perimeter of these figures.

Workbook Exercise 13-14 [3rd Exercise 5-6]

Activity 2.3d **Area of compound figures**

1. Discuss **tasks 11-12, textbook p. 35 [3rd p. 19]**.
   - Note that the answer to task 12 should be left in terms of π.

     #12. Area = (area of large semicircle with radius 2 cm) – (area of small semicircle with radius 1 cm)

     $= (\frac{1}{2} \times \pi \times 2 \times 2) - (\frac{1}{2} \times \pi \times 1 \times 1) = (2 \times \pi) - (\frac{1}{2} \times \pi) = 1\frac{1}{2}\pi \text{ or } \frac{3\pi}{2} \text{cm}^2$
   - You can also ask students to find the perimeters of these figures.

2. Have students do **problems 1-5, Practice 2C, textbook p. 37 [3rd Practice 1C p. 21]**.
   - You can also ask students to find the perimeter of these figures.

Workbook Exercise 15 [3rd Exercise 7]

Activity 2.3e **Practice**

1. Have students find the areas of figures B-F on p. 43 of this guide. They can also find the perimeters if they have not already done so.

Workbook Exercise 16 [3rd Exercise 8]

All of these figures are formed from circles, semicircles, quarter-circles, squares, or right triangles. The circles in figure C are all equal sizes. For each figure, find the perimeter and/or area of the shaded part. Decide whether to use $\frac{22}{7}$ or 3.14 for π.

A

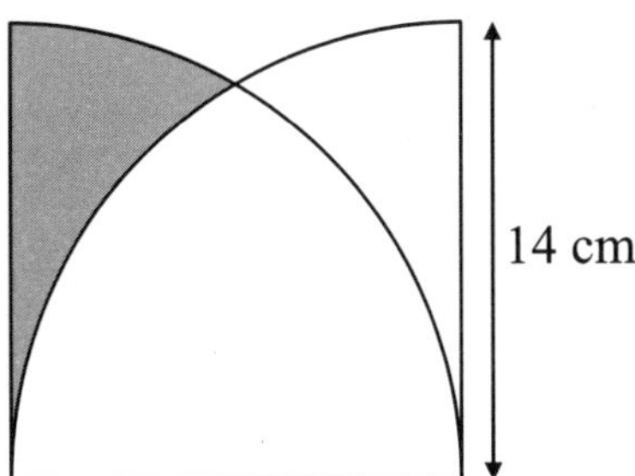

Perimeter = __________

B

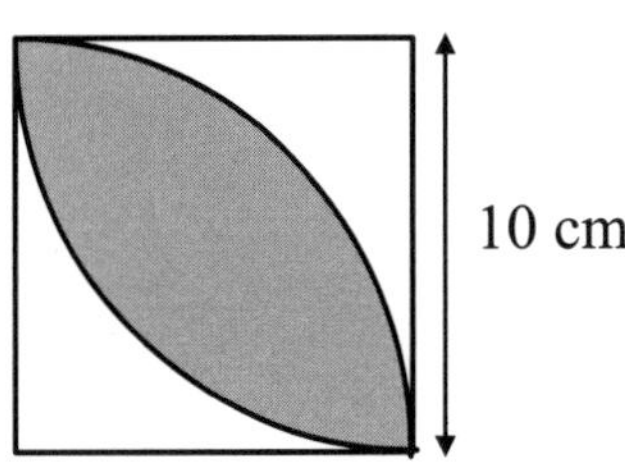

Perimeter = __________

Area = ______________

C

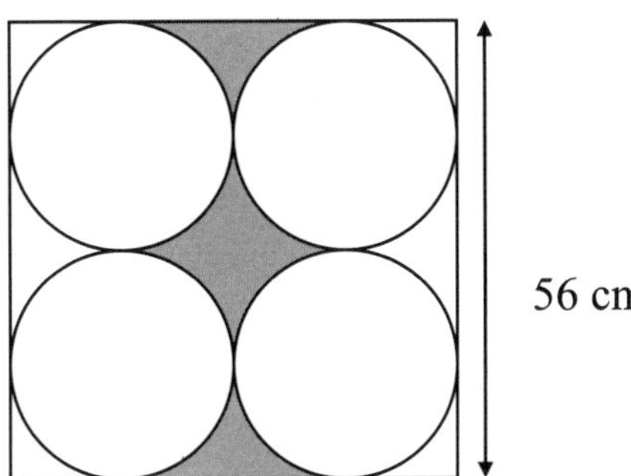

Perimeter = __________

Area = ______________

D

14 cm 14 cm

Perimeter = __________

Area = ______________

E

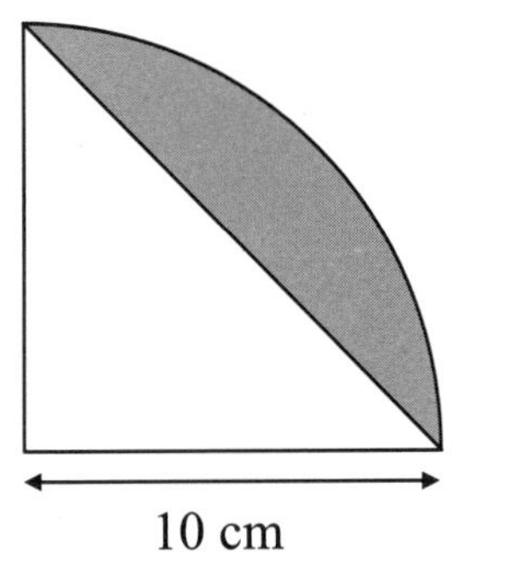

Area = ______________

F

16 cm

20 cm

Area = ______________

Answers:

A. The two quarter-circles are identical, so the perimeter of the shaded part is one fourth the circumference of a circle with radius 14 cm plus the side.

$P = (\frac{1}{4} \times \frac{22}{7} \times 2 \times 14) + 14 = 22 + 14 = 36$ cm

B. The shaded area is the overlap of two quarter-circles. The perimeter is the circumference for both quarter-circles, or for a semicircle with radius 10 cm.

$P = \frac{1}{2} \times 3.14 \times 2 \times 10 = 31.4$ cm

To find the area of the shaded portion, we can first subtract area of a quarter-circle from that of the square to get the area of one of the unshaded sides, and then subtract two of those from the area of the square.

Area of 1 unshaded portion $= (10 \times 10) - (\frac{1}{4} \times 3.14 \times 10 \times 10) = 100 - 78.5 = 21.5\text{ cm}^2$

Area of shaded portion $= 100 - (2 \times 21.5) = 57\text{ cm}^2$

C. The shaded part is bordered by 4 semicircles and 2 straight sides. The length of the straight side is half the length of the side of the square, since it would be from the center of one circle to the center of the other.

$P = (2 \times \frac{22}{7} \times 28) + 28 = 176 + 28 = 204$ cm

The area of the shaded part is the area a rectangle 28 by 56, minus the area of four semicircles, or 2 whole circles.

$A = (28 \times 56) - (2 \times \frac{22}{7} \times 14 \times 14) = 1568 - 1232 = 336\text{ cm}^2$

D. The perimeter is the circumference of the large semicircle plus that of the two smaller semicircles, which make one whole small circle.

Perimeter $= (\frac{1}{2} \times \frac{22}{7} \times 28) + (\frac{22}{7} \times 14) = 44 + 44 = 88$ cm

The small shaded semicircle can be fit into the part cut out of the larger circle. So the area is just the area of the larger semicircle.

Area $= \frac{1}{2} \times \frac{22}{7} \times 14 \times 14 = 308\text{ cm}^2$

E. The area of the shaded part is the area of the quarter circle minus the area of the triangle.

$A = (\frac{1}{4} \times 3.14 \times 10 \times 10) - (\frac{1}{2} \times 10 \times 10) = 78.5 - 50 = 28.5\text{ cm}^2$

F. The area of the shaded parts is the area of both semicircles minus the area of the triangle. The area of both semicircles includes the overlap twice, but subtracting the triangle takes care of one overlap.

$A = (\frac{1}{2} \times 3.14 \times 8 \times 8) + (\frac{1}{2} \times 3.14 \times 10 \times 10) - (\frac{1}{2} \times 20 \times 16)$

$= 100.48 + 157 - 160 = 97.48\text{ cm}^2$

Graphs

Objectives

- Read and interpret pie charts with data given as whole numbers, fractions, or percentages.
- Create pie charts from data.

Suggested number of sessions: 4

	Objectives	Textbook	Workbook	Activities
Part 1 : Pie Charts				**4 sessions**
25	▪ Understand pie charts. ▪ Read and interpret pie charts with data given as whole numbers.	[US]p. 38 [US]p. 39, tasks 1-2 [3d]p. 22 [3d]p. 23, tasks 1-2	[US]Ex. 17 [3d]Ex. 9	3.1a
26	▪ Read and interpret pie charts with data given as fractions. ▪ Create a fraction pie chart.	[US]p. 40, tasks 3-4 [3d]p. 24, tasks 3-4	[US]Ex. 18 [3d]Ex. 10	3.1b
27 28	▪ Read and interpret pie charts with data given as percentage. ▪ Create a percentage pie chart.	[US]p. 41, tasks 5-6 [3d]p. 25, tasks 5-6	[US]Ex. 19 [3d]Ex. 11	3.1c

Part 1: Pie Charts — 4 sessions

Objectives

- Understand pie charts.
- Read and interpret pie charts with data given as whole numbers.
- Read and interpret pie charts with data given as fractions.
- Read and interpret pie charts with data given as percentages.
- Create pie charts from data.

Materials

- Circle graph with 24 divisions
- Circle graph with 100 divisions
- Examples of pie charts in texts from other subjects

Homework

US edition	**3rd edition**
• Workbook Exercise 17	Workbook Exercise 9
• Workbook Exercise 18	Workbook Exercise 10
• Workbook Exercise 19	Workbook Exercise 11

Notes

A pie chart is used to show the composition of a set of data such that each component is represented as part of a whole. The data are represented by the proportional parts of a circle.

Three forms of pie chart are introduced in this unit: ones that display numbers, (e.g., task 1, p. 39 [3rd p. 23]), ones that display fractions (e.g., p. 40 [3rd p. 24]), and ones that display percentages (e.g., task 5, p. 41 [3rd p. 25]).

Although use of degrees for calculation is not covered here, the little square symbolizing a right angle is used to show the 90° angle of a quarter of the circle.

If your state's standards require using degrees to construct pie charts, you may want to include a lesson on that here. A whole circle is 360°. Once the fraction of the whole is found for each piece of data, we can multiply that fraction by 360° to find the central angle used for that component on the pie chart. So for the pie chart on p. 38 [3rd p. 22], we can use the fractions to determine what their central angle is so that we can construct a pie chart.

Size S: $\frac{1}{4} \times 360° = 90°$ Size M: $\frac{1}{2} \times 360° = 180°$

Size XL: $\frac{1}{12} \times 360° = 30°$ Size L: $\frac{1}{6} \times 360° = 60°$

Fraction Circle Chart

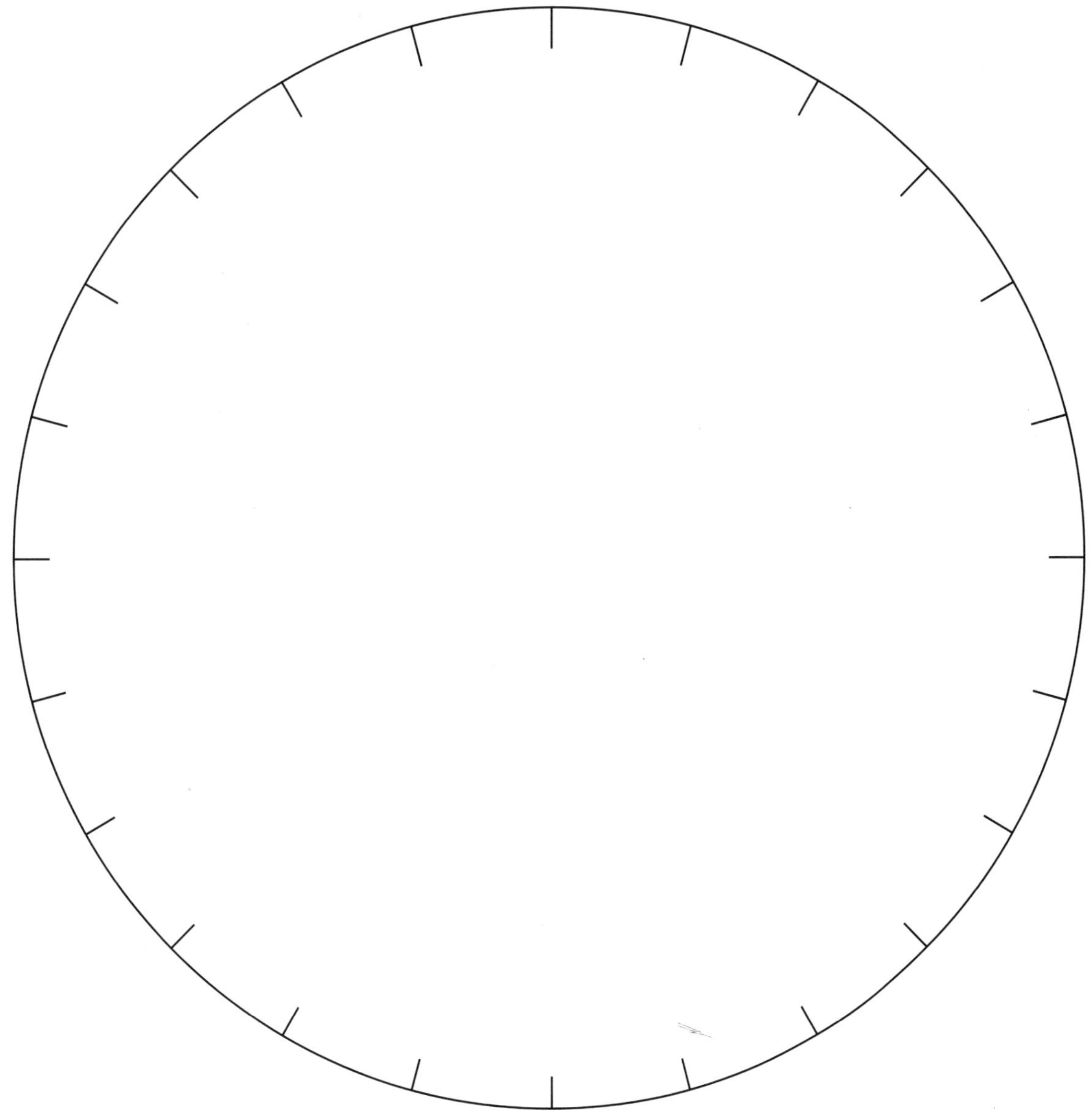

Fraction/Percentage Circle Chart

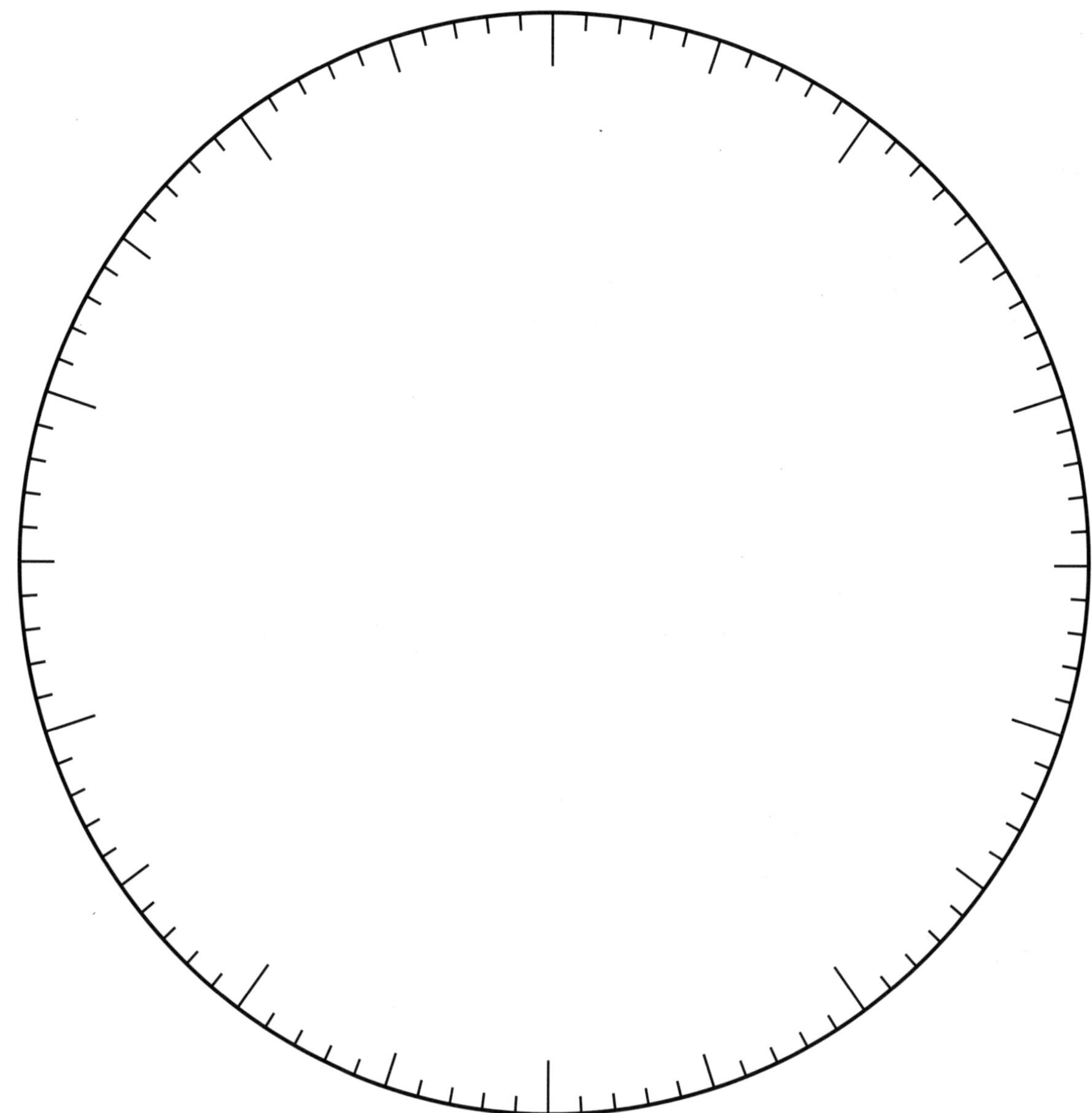

Activity 3.1a **Pie charts**

1. Discuss pie charts.
   - Review other types of graphs students have learned about in the past – picture graphs, bar graphs, and line graphs. Draw or show some examples of each kind of graph. Discuss the relative merits of displaying data in a table versus, and as an aid to, one of these kinds of graphs.
   - Refer to **textbook p. 38 [3rd p. 22]**.
   - You can discuss this page, or draw the chart on the board, writing the fractions under each size as you guide the students in finding the answers to the questions, and guide students in making a pie chart from the data using copies of the fraction circle on p. 47 of this guide.
   - Lead students to see that the circle represents the whole, which is the total number of shirts sold: $\frac{1}{4}+\frac{1}{2}+\frac{1}{12}+\frac{1}{6}=1$.
   - Point out that the lines bordering the section representing $\frac{1}{4}$ make a right angle at the center. A fourth of 360° is 90°.
   - Ask students what type of information they can get from the pie chart if they did not have the table. Ask questions such as, "Which size did the shop sell the most of?" They can see the relative amounts sold for each size. Without the table, though, they do not know how big the data sample was; that is, how many shirts total were sold, or how many shirts of each size were sold. A chart such as this can tell them what proportions they should use to restock the shirts. If, for example, they wanted to order 1000 shirts, they would most likely order 500 size M shirts. They would order fewer XL shirts than the other sizes.
   - If you have examples of pie charts from other subjects, such as history or science, show them to the students and discuss the type of information that can be seen at a glance from the chart. For example, science texts often have pie charts for the composition of earth's atmosphere, and from the chart we easily see that a little over $\frac{3}{4}$ of the earth's atmosphere is nitrogen, whereas oxygen is about $\frac{1}{5}$ of the earth's atmosphere.

2. Discuss **task 1, textbook p. 39 [3rd p. 23]**.
   - Point out that pie charts would normally either include numbers for all the items, or for none of the items (if the purpose of the chart was just to get a general idea of relative amounts.)
   - Draw the chart on the board. Guide students in answering the questions.
     (a) Plastic chairs are in the greatest quantity.
     (b) Use the total amount to find the number of wooden chairs.
     200 – 80 – 30 – 40 = 50
     There are 50 wooden chairs.
     (c) To find the fraction of the total, we put the part (plastic chairs, 80), over the total (200).
     $\frac{80}{200}=\frac{2}{5}$ $\frac{2}{5}$ of the chairs are plastic.
     (d) We are comparing the number of plastic chairs to the number of wicker [3rd rattan] chairs.
     $\frac{80}{40}=2$ There are twice as many plastic chairs.

3. Discuss **task 2, textbook p. 39 [3rd p. 23]**.
   - Draw the chart on the board. Guide students in answering the questions.
     (a) The angle at the center for the games is 90°, which is $\frac{1}{4}$ of the total.

     (b) Use the value given for $\frac{1}{4}$ of the total to find the total

     $\frac{1}{4} \longrightarrow \$3000$

     $1 \longrightarrow \$3000 \times 4 = \$12{,}000$

     The total money collected was $12,000

     (c) $\$12{,}000 - (2 \times \$3000) - \$4800 = \$1200$ (collected by music booths)

     (d) $4800 : 3000 = 8 : 5$

Workbook Exercise 17 [3rd Exercise 9]

Activity 3.1b **Fraction pie charts**

1. Discuss **task 3, textbook p. 40 [3rd p. 24]**.
   - Draw the chart on the board. Guide students in answering the questions.
     (a) Most students had toast [3rd bread] for breakfast.
     (b) The fraction of students that had eggs [3rd cake] for breakfast is the whole (1) minus the fractions for the other choices.
     $1 - \frac{3}{5} - \frac{1}{4} - \frac{1}{10} = \frac{20}{20} - \frac{12}{20} - \frac{5}{20} - \frac{2}{20} = \frac{1}{20}$

     (c) $\frac{3}{5} \times 40 = 24$ (number of students that had toast)

     (d) $\frac{1}{4} = 25\%$ (percent of students that had cereal [3rd rice])

2. Discuss **task 4, textbook p. 40 [3rd p. 24]**.
   - Draw the chart on the board. Guide students in answering the questions.
     (a) $\frac{1}{2}$

     (b) The angle at the center shown for the English is 90°, which is $\frac{1}{4}$ of the total, or 25%.

     (c) Half the students liked Mathematics best, so the other half liked one of the rest of the subjects best. Since a fourth liked English best, that leaves a fourth for Others and Science. We know that Others is $\frac{1}{8}$, so Science must be $\frac{1}{4} - \frac{1}{8} = \frac{1}{8}$.

     (d) $\frac{1}{2} \longrightarrow 1200$

     $\frac{1}{4} \longrightarrow 1200 \div 2 = 600$ 600 students liked English best.

3. Construct a fraction pie chart.
   - Provide students with copies of the fraction circle graph on p. 47 of this guide.
   - Have them estimate how many hours a day during a normal week day they spend on 4-5 activities, such as sleep, school, meals, homework, other. Have them find the time spent for each activity as a fraction of a day, and then show the fractions on a fraction circle chart. They can compare charts. To have a greater variety of charts, you could then have them choose 4-5 activities for the a weekend day, including sleep and the catch-all "other", estimate the time spent on each activity, and create a fraction pie chart showing how they spend their time.

Workbook Exercise 18 [3rd Exercise 10]

Activity 3.1c **Percentage pie charts**

1. Discuss **task 5, textbook p. 41 [3rd p. 25]**.
   - Draw the pie chart on the board. Guide students in answering the questions.
     (a) The most popular sport is swimming (35%).
     (b) Percentage of students that chose basketball = 100% – 30% – 20% – 35% = 15%
     (c) We can find the number of students who chose baseball [3rd badminton] by finding the fraction of the whole: $\frac{30}{100} \times 200 = 60$ students
     (d) $35\% = \frac{35}{100} = \frac{7}{20}$ $\frac{7}{20}$ of the students chose swimming.

2. Discuss **task 6, textbook p. 41 [3rd p. 25]**.
   - Draw the chart on the board. Guide students in answering the questions.
     (a) She spent the most money on shirts [3rd blouses].
     (b) Skirts and shirts together are half the circle, or 50%.
     Percentage of total money spent on shirts = 50% – 15% = 35%
     (c) Pants and dresses together are 50%.
     Percentage of total money spent on pants = 50% – 20% = 30%
     OR, Percentage of the total money spent on pants = 100% minus the percentage for skirts, shirts, and dresses = 100% – 15% – 35% – 20% = 30%
     (d) We are given a value ($60) for the pants, so we know 30% of the total spent is $60. We can use the unitary approach to find what 100% is, as students learned in *Primary Mathematics 6A*.
     $30\% \longrightarrow \$60$
     $100\% \longrightarrow \$\frac{60}{30} \times 100 = \$200$
     She spent $200 altogether.

3. Construct a percentage pie chart with data you provide.
   - You can pass out sheets with a data table, and just a circle drawn under it for them to divide into sections and fill in. Or, put a data table on copies of the Fraction/Percentage Circle Chart on p. 48 of this guide.

4. Have students collect data, organize it into a data table, and have them make a pie chart based on the data.
   - You can have them work in groups. Each group could decide what type of data to collect and how large a sample size to use. There should not be more than 6 data items. For example, one group could list 6 ice cream flavors and poll other students for their favorite flavor of the 6. They then create a table for their data, determine the percentage part for each item, and create a pie graph. You can give them copies of the Fraction/Percentage Circle Graph on p. 48 of this guide. They can present their information to the class.
   - If you have access to software that creates graphs, such as Microsoft Excel, you can have students create pie charts using the software.
   - If you wish to teach them how to construct their own pie charts, they can calculate the angle needed for each item and use a compass and protractor.

Workbook Exercise 19 [3rd Exercise 11]

Review

Objectives

- Review previous material.

Suggested number of sessions: 4

	Objectives	Textbook	Workbook	Activities
Review				**5 sessions**
29-32	▪ Review	US pp. 42-47, Review A US pp. 48-53, Review B 3d pp. 26-31, Review A 3d pp. 32-57, Review B	Review 1 Review 2	

Notes

Reviews in *Primary Mathematics* cover material from all previous levels, so the reviews are lengthy. Reviews are particularly important in *Primary Mathematics 6B* since students are finishing up their primary education in preparation for more advanced mathematics. These reviews will allow you to see if your students are weak in any topic. The most effective way to re-teach any topic (unless you are quite familiar both with the material and the way it was covered in earlier levels), is to go back to the levels in which it was covered.

You can work through the reviews all at once, or have your students do 5-6 problems from the review daily or several pages weekly so that you carry on a continuing review as you proceed with the next units.

The reviews in the textbook tend to be a more challenging than the reviews in the workbook, and the problems can be good opportunities for discussion of concepts and solutions.

Possible solutions to selected problems are given in this guide. They show only one or two methods. Students may find a different, valid way to solve some of the problems. Some of the solutions in this guide include shortcuts for your benefit – do not require students to use the shortcut but realize that it is OK for the student to use shortcuts if they can do so and get the right answer. Students who have learned the previous levels well should have no problem with shortcuts. For example, if they go from 3 cards cost \$2 to 60 cards cost $\$2 \times 20$, that is a valid approach. It is also valid to go directly from 3 cards cost \$2 to 60 cards cost $\$\frac{2}{3} \times 60$ without having to first show that 1 card cost $\$\frac{2}{3}$. Students who have learned the previous levels will regularly use shortcuts like this; other students will need to find and show the calculation for 1 unit first or will feel more comfortable writing the intermediate step.

You can compare and discuss different methods. Have students come to the board and demonstrate their solutions. Guide them if they make an error or get lost in the explanation. Do not expect or insist on a formulaic approach to solving problems.

Review A, pp. 42-47 [3rd pp. 26-31]

19. Total = 72 marbles
1 unit = number of blue marbles
2 units = 72 – 20 = 52
1 unit = 52 ÷ 2 = 26
There were 26 blue marbles.

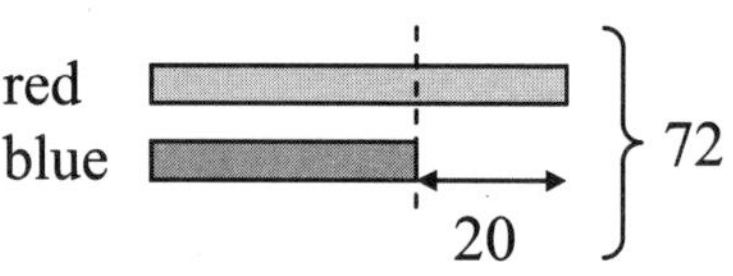

22. Total weight of 3 boys = 3 × average weight = 3 × 35.6 = 106.8 kg
Weight of 2 boys = 106.8 – 34.8 = 72 kg
Average weight of 2 boys = $\frac{72}{2}$ = 36 kg

24.

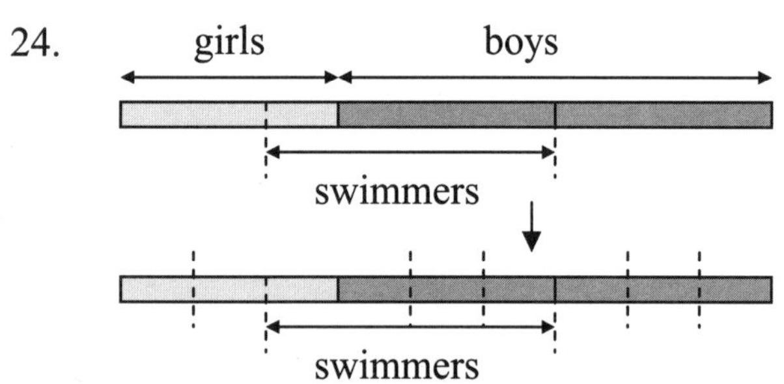

Since $\frac{1}{3}$ of the girls can swim, and girls are $\frac{1}{3}$ of all the students, divide each third into thirds. Swimmers are 4 out of 9 units. So the fraction of students that can swim is $\frac{4}{9}$.

OR:

Fraction of students who are girls that can swim $= \frac{1}{3} \times \frac{1}{3} = \frac{1}{9}$

Fraction of students that are boys $= 1 - \frac{1}{3} = \frac{2}{3}$

Fraction of students who are boys that can swim $= \frac{1}{2} \times \frac{2}{3} = \frac{1}{3}$

Fraction of students that can swim $= \frac{1}{9} + \frac{1}{3} = \frac{1}{9} + \frac{3}{9} = \frac{4}{9}$

25.

book

money left

Radio = $50

5 units = $50
1 unit = $10
2 units = $20
He had $20 left.

OR:

Fraction spent on radio = $1 - \frac{1}{8} - \frac{1}{4} = \frac{5}{8}$

$\frac{5}{8} \longrightarrow$ $50 or: $50 \div \frac{5}{8} = 50 \times \frac{8}{5}$ = $80 = all his money

$\frac{1}{8} \longrightarrow$ $50 ÷ 5 = $10 $\frac{1}{4} \times$ $80 = $20 = money he had left

$\frac{2}{8} \longrightarrow$ $10 × 2 = $20

26. 3 units = 270

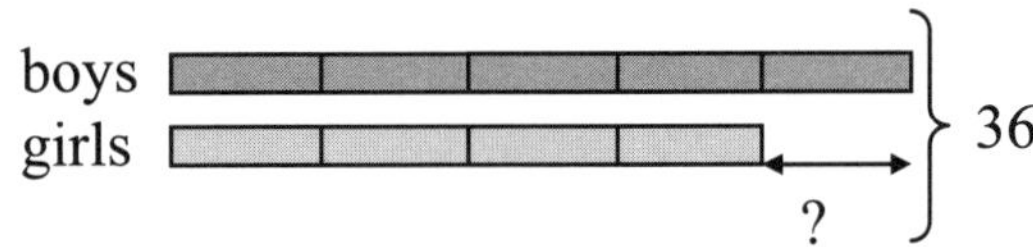

4 units = $\frac{270}{3} \times 4 = 360$

There are 360 girls.

27. 9 units = 36

boys
girls
36
?

1 unit = $36 \div 9 = 4$

There are 4 more boys than girls.

33. John bought 3 more books than Peter. Together they bought 11 books.

3 books cost $1.95.

1 book costs $1.95 ÷ 3 = $0.65

11 books cost $0.65 × 11 = $7.15

34.

$300 remainder

half of remainder $120 $160

Half of remainder = $120 + $160 = $280

Remainder = $280 × 2 = $560

Salary = $300 + $560 = $860

35. $\frac{3}{4} \longrightarrow \$1800$

$\frac{4}{4} \longrightarrow \$\frac{1800}{3} \times 4 = \$2400$

$\frac{2}{5} \longrightarrow \frac{2}{5} \times \$2400 = \$960$

36. US: *Before*: 3d:

Tyrone Gopal

Ryan Raju

After:

Tyrone

Ryan

The new ratio will be 3 : 4

37. She saves 60% of the remainder. The remainder is 30%.

60% of 30% = $\frac{6}{10} \times 30\% = 18\%$ 18% of the salary is $360.

$18\% \longrightarrow \$360$

$100\% \longrightarrow \$\frac{360}{18} \times 100 = \$2000$

Her monthly salary is $2000.

38.

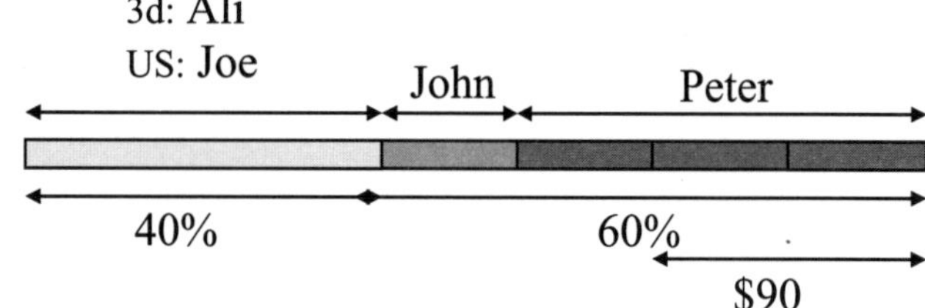

$90 is half of 60% of the money.

30% ⟶ $90

40% ⟶ $\$\frac{90}{30} \times 40 = \$120$

Joe receives $120.

39. $\frac{2}{5}$ of the trip = 30 km

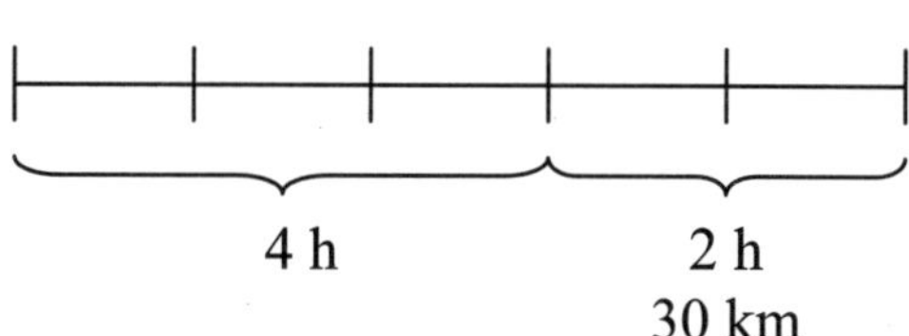

All of the trip = $\frac{30}{2} \times 5 = 75$ km

Total time = 6 h

Average speed = $\frac{75 \text{ km}}{6 \text{ h}} = 12.5$ km/h

42. Perimeter of triangle = 12 + 14 + 10 = 36 cm
Side of square = 36 ÷ 4 = 9 cm
Area of square = $9 \times 9 = 81$ cm^2

Review B, pp. 48-53 [3rd pp. 32-37]

14. $\frac{3}{4}\,\ell \longrightarrow 4$ glasses

4 glasses

$\frac{1}{4}\,\ell \longrightarrow \frac{4}{3}$ glasses

$3\,\ell \longrightarrow \frac{4}{3} \times 12 = 16$ glasses

16. $2 ⟶ 5 oranges

$24 ⟶ $\frac{5}{2} \times 24 = 60$ oranges

17. $40 ⟶ 1 certificate [voucher]

$350 ⟶ $\frac{1}{40} \times 350 = 8.75$

She will get 8 of them.

19. Total of 3 numbers = $45 \times 3 = 135$
Total of 2 of the numbers = $47 \times 2 = 94$
Third number = $135 - 94 = 41$

20. $8\ \ell \longrightarrow 1$ min
$200\ \ell \longrightarrow \frac{1}{8} \times 200 = 25$ min
It will take 25 min to fill the tank.

22. The remainder after buying the book is $\frac{3}{4}$.
The cost of the photo album = $\frac{1}{2}$ of the remainder = $\frac{1}{2}$ of $\frac{3}{4} = \frac{1}{2} \times \frac{3}{4} = \frac{3}{8}$
Fraction spent = $\frac{1}{4} + \frac{3}{8} = \frac{2}{8} + \frac{3}{8} = \frac{5}{8}$

24. 12 units = 60 yd [3rd: m]
1 unit = $\frac{60}{12}$
7 units = $\frac{60}{12} \times 7 = 35$
The longest piece is 35 yd [3rd : 35 m]

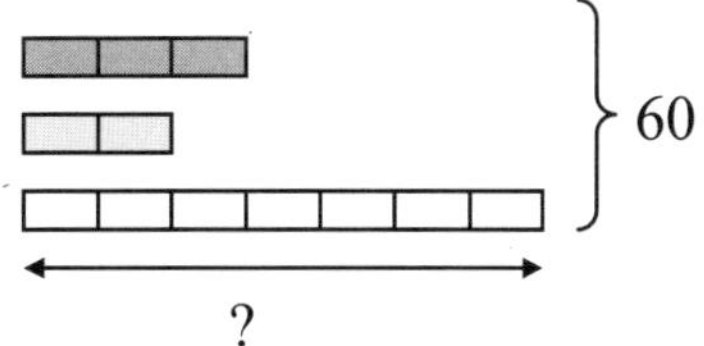

29. Total stickers do not change.
Total stickers = $130 + 50 = 180$
3 units = 180
1 unit = $180 \div 3 = 60$
Kara [Devi] had 50 and ended up with 60, so
Jack [Samy] gave her 10 stickers.

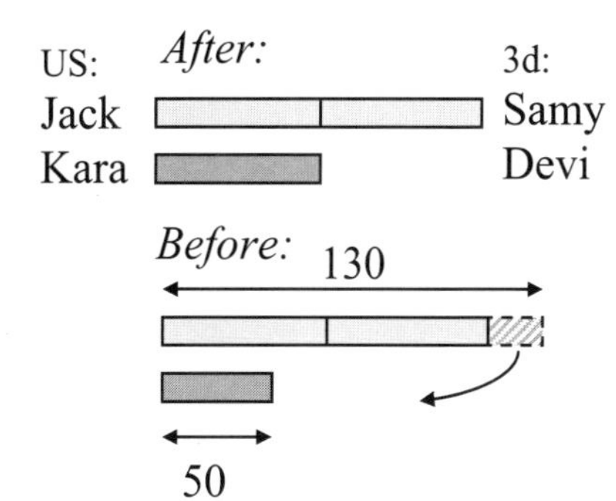

30. He bought 100 cards for $60
Number sold at 3 for \$2 = $\frac{3}{5} \times 100 = 60$ cards
He sold 60 at 3 for \$2, and $100 - 60 = 40$ at \$0.75 each.
$3 \longrightarrow \$2$
$60 \longrightarrow \$\frac{2}{3} \times 60 = \$40$ OR: $60 \longrightarrow \$2 \times 20 = \$40$
$40 \times \$0.75 = \$30$
Total money = $\$40 + \$30 = \$70$
Amount of money he made = $\$70 - \$60 = \$10$

31. 1 unit = 24
2 units = 48 = remainder
$\frac{1}{3}$ of remainder = $\frac{1}{3} \times 48 = 16$
There are 16 yellow beads.

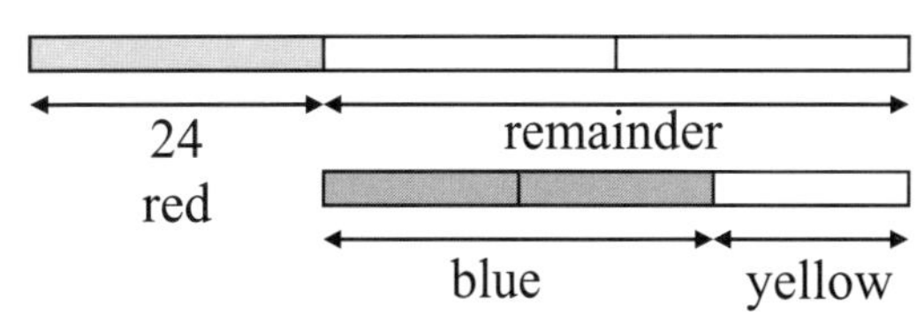

32. The number of boys does not change.

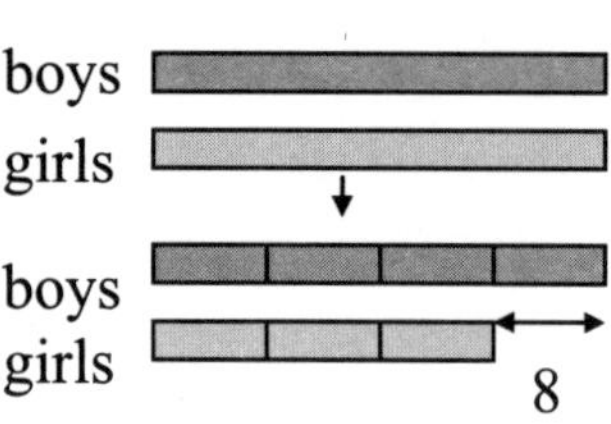

boys : girls
before *1* : 1 = 4 : 4
after *4* : 3 = 4 : 3
The number of girls is reduced by 1 unit.
1 unit = 8
3 units = 8 × 3 = 24
24 girls remained in the band.

33. Total weight = 40 × 2 = 80 lb [3rd: kg]

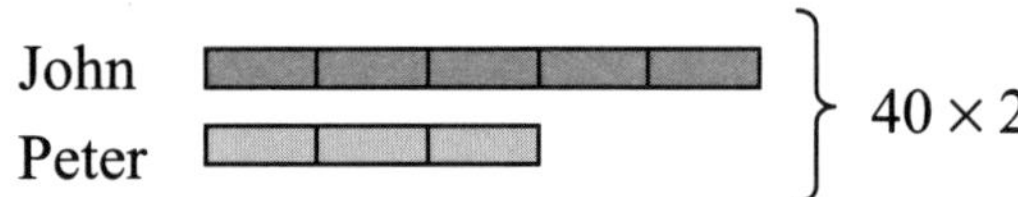

8 units = 80
1 unit = 80 ÷ 8 = 10
5 units = 10 × 5 = 50
John weighs 50 lb [3rd: 50 kg].

34. Mary $60
Susan

2 units = $60
8 units = $60 × 4 = $240
They saved $240.

35. Percentage boys that walk to school = 10% of the boys = 10% of 60% = $\frac{1}{10} \times 60\% = 6\%$

Percentage girls that walk to school = 30% of the girls = 30% of 40% = $\frac{3}{10} \times 40\% = 12\%$

Percentage of the students that walk to school = 6% + 12% = 18%

36. The base (100%) is February, since we are finding the percent more *than in* February.
Difference = $75 – $60 = $15
Percentage difference = $\frac{15}{60} \times 100\% = 25\%$
He saved 25% more in January than in February

37. 40 min = $\frac{40}{60}$ h = $\frac{2}{3}$ h

20 min = $\frac{20}{60}$ h = $\frac{1}{3}$ h

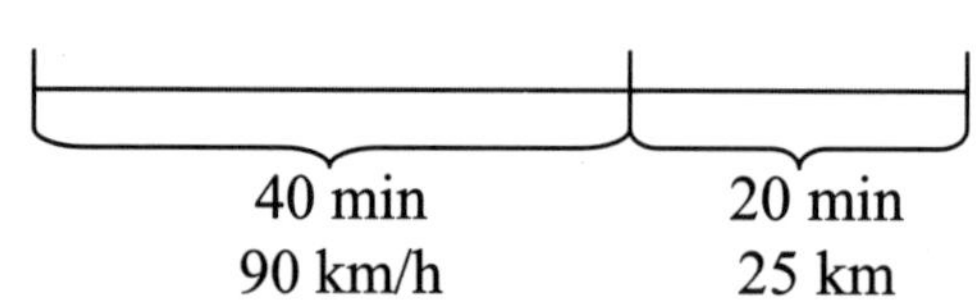

Distance for 1st part = 90 km/h × $\frac{2}{3}$ h = 60 km
Total distance = 60 km + 25 km = 85 km
Total time = 1 h
Average speed = 85 km/h

Workbook Review 1

13.

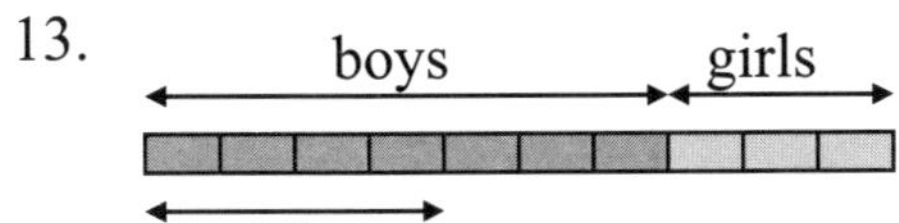

4 units = 16

10 units = $\frac{16}{4} \times 10 = 40$

There are 40 students.

OR: $\frac{7}{10}$ of the students are boys.

$\frac{3}{10}$ of the students are girls.

$\frac{7}{10} - \frac{3}{10} = \frac{4}{10}$

$\frac{4}{10} \longrightarrow 16$

$\frac{10}{10} \longrightarrow \frac{16}{4} \times 10 = 40$ students

14. 11 units = 132

3 units = $\frac{132}{11} \times 3 = 36$

There are 36 more adults than children.

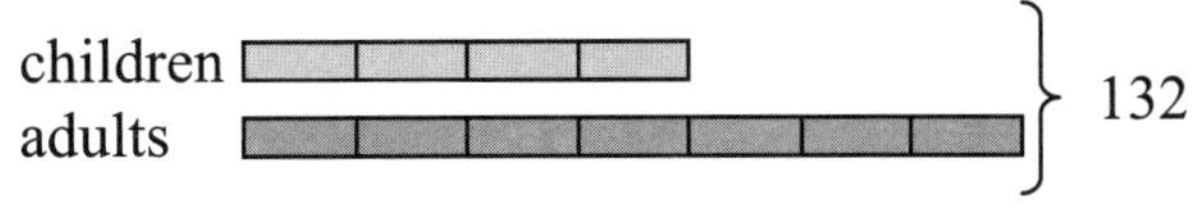

15. 225% of the girls is 450.

$225\% \longrightarrow 450$

$25\% \longrightarrow \frac{450}{225} \times 25 = 50$

There are 50 more boys than girls.

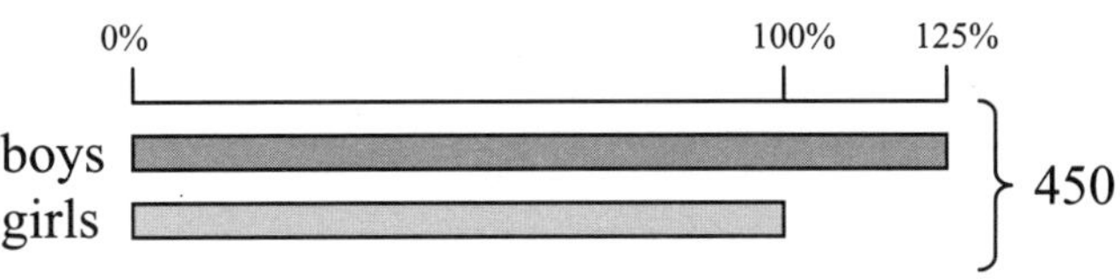

23. Money from tarts = 200 × \$0.40 = \$80
Money spent on plates = \$80 – \$28.80 = \$51.20
Cost of 1 plate = \$51.20 ÷ 8 = \$6.40

24. $\frac{2}{5}$ of the boys = $\frac{2}{10}$ of all the students

$\frac{1}{2}$ of the girls = $\frac{1}{4}$ of all the students

Fraction of the students that go by bus [3rd: MRT] $= \frac{2}{10} + \frac{1}{4} = \frac{4}{20} + \frac{5}{20} = \frac{9}{20}$

25. Ben's share = \$60 – \$15 = \$45
Rajah's share = \$45 × 3 = \$135

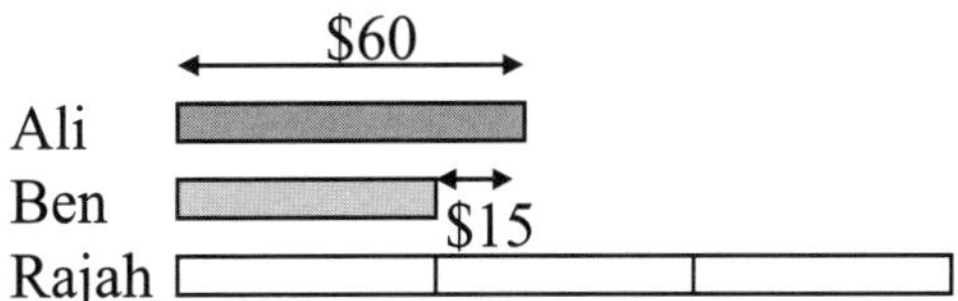

26. 10% of the children last year = 11

$10\% \longrightarrow 11$

$100\% \longrightarrow 110$

There were 110 members last year.

Number of boys last year = $\frac{1}{2}$ of the total members last year = $\frac{1}{2} \times 110 = 55$

Workbook Review 2

5. Half of the two middle fourths, and one half of the last fourth is shaded.
$\frac{1}{2} \times \frac{2}{4} + \frac{1}{2} \times \frac{1}{4} = \frac{2}{8} + \frac{1}{8} = \frac{3}{8}$

9. Cost of shorts = 1 unit
Cost of T-shirt = 1 unit + \$5
4 units = \$54 – (3 × \$5)
= \$54 – \$15
= \$39
1 unit = $\$\frac{39}{4}$ = \$9.75
The shorts cost \$9.75.

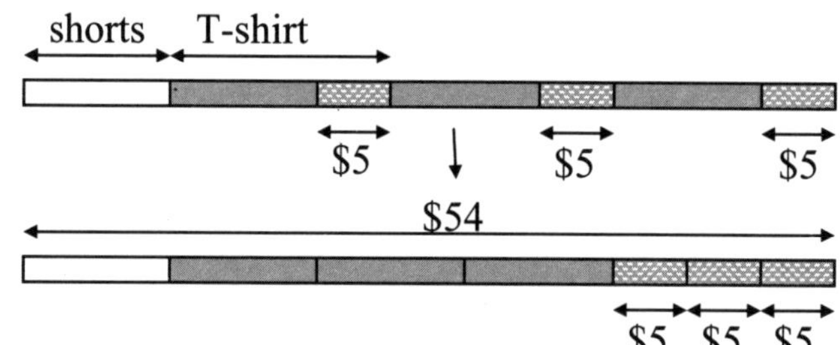

10. His remainder after giving away $\frac{2}{3}$ is $\frac{1}{3}$ of the mangoes = $\frac{1}{3} \times 54 = 18$ mangoes
Amount left after eating $\frac{1}{6}$ of the remainder is $\frac{5}{6}$ of remainder = $\frac{5}{6} \times 18 = 15$ mangoes
OR:
One third (the remainder) is divided into 6 small units to show the $\frac{1}{6}$ of the remainder that are eaten. 5 small units are left.

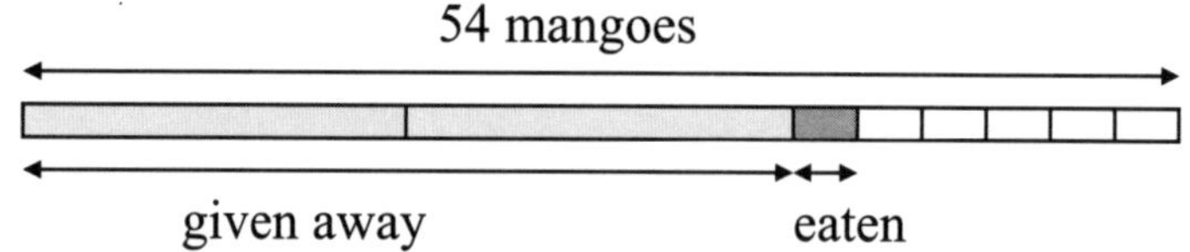

Divide the whole bar into small units, giving 3 × 6 = 18 units.
18 units = 54 mangoes
5 units = $\frac{54}{18} \times 5 = 15$
15 mangoes are left.

11. Fraction of total capacity poured out = $\frac{1}{2} - \frac{1}{3} = \frac{3}{6} - \frac{2}{6} = \frac{1}{6}$
$\frac{1}{6}$ of capacity = 200 ml
Total capacity = 200 × 6 = 1200 ml

12. [3rd edition: Austin is Ahmad]
There are 8 units total, so for each to have the same number Austin gives Henry 1 unit.
8 units = 1000 stamps
1 unit = 125 stamps
Austin [Ahmad] gives Henry 125 stamps.

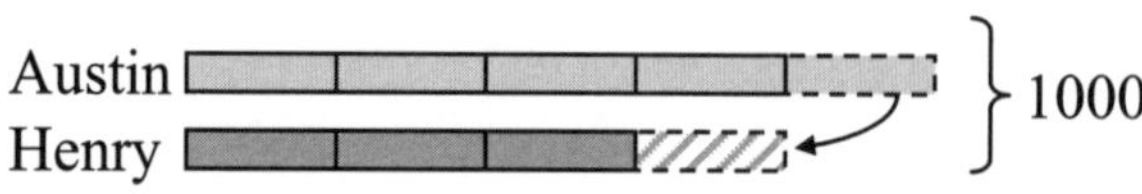

14. 25% of Susan's savings is \$200. Susan has 100% of Susan's savings, and Mary has 125% of Susan's savings. Together they have 225% of Susan's savings.

$25\% \longrightarrow \$200$

$225\% \longrightarrow \$\frac{200}{25} \times 225 = \$1800$

Their total savings is \$1800.

17. Total weight of 3 girls = $3x$
Total weight of 4 girls = $30 \times 4 = 120$ kg
Weight of 4th girl = 120 kg – $3x$ kg.

24.

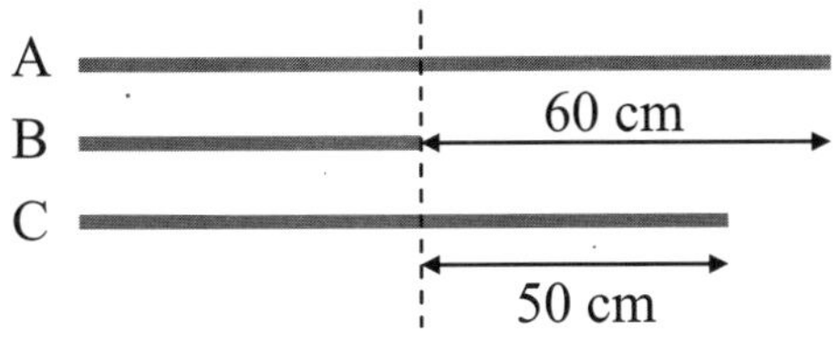

Let the length of B be 1 unit. A is then 1 unit + 60 cm, and C is 1 unit + 50 cm.
If 60 cm is cut off of A, and 50 cm is cut off of B, there would be 3 units, that is, three ribbons of the same length as B. So the total length – 60 cm – 50 cm gives 3 ribbons of the same length.
Total length = 2.6 m = 260 cm
3 units = 260 – 60 – 50 = 150 cm
1 unit = 150 ÷ 3 = 50 cm
Ribbon A is 50 + 60 = 110 cm long.
OR:
If A is the unit, then we need to add 60 cm to B and 10 cm to C to get 3 units.
3 units = 260 + 70 = 330
1 unit = 110 cm = length of A.

25. Fraction sold on Monday = $\frac{3}{5}$, fraction sold on Tuesday $= 1 - \frac{3}{5} = \frac{2}{5}$

Fraction fewer sold on Tuesday = $\frac{3}{5} - \frac{2}{5} = \frac{1}{5}$

$\frac{1}{5}$ of the postcards = 25

$\frac{5}{5}$ of the postcards = $25 \times 5 = 125$

He had 125 postcards.

26. $\frac{3}{4}$ of the beads are yellow and blue.

red beads | yellow and blue beads

60%: yellow | 40%: blue

40% of the yellow and blue beads are blue.

40% of $\frac{3}{4} = \frac{40}{100} \times \frac{3}{4} = \frac{3}{10}$

$\frac{3}{10}$ of the beads = 48

$\frac{10}{10}$ of the beads = $\frac{48}{3} \times 10 = 160$

OR:

Divide remainder into 30 little units (lowest common multiple of 3 and 10).
Each third is divided into 10 parts; there is a total of 40 units.
60% of 30 units = 18 units, and 40% of 30 units = 12 units (blue beads)
12 units = 48 beads

40 units = $\frac{48}{12} \times 40 = 160$ beads.

There are 160 beads.

27. Time for car = 1 h

Distance for car = 60 km/h × 1 h = 60 km

Time for van = $\frac{60 \text{ km}}{40 \text{ km/h}} = \frac{3}{2}$ h = 1 h 30 min

Time van arrived at B = 2:20 + 1 h 30 min
= 3:50 p.m.

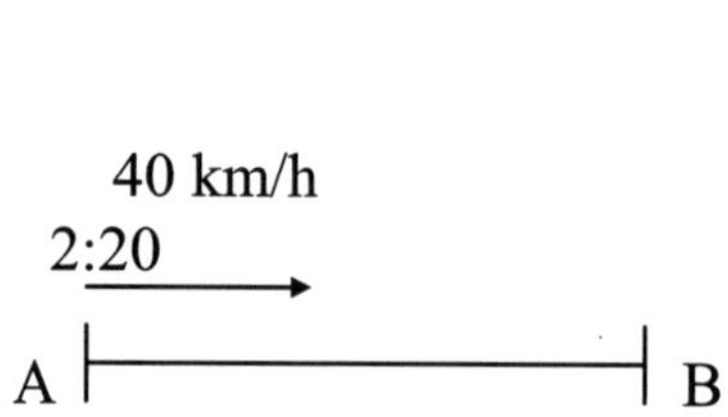

Volume

Objectives

- Find the volume of a cuboid.
- Find an unknown dimension of a cuboid when given its volume and two dimensions or its volume and the area of a face.
- Solve multi-step word problems involving the volume of liquids, the displacement of a liquid, or the rate of flow of a liquid.

Suggested number of sessions: 6

	Objectives	**Textbook**	**Workbook**	**Activities**
Part 1 : Solving Problems				**6 sessions**
33	▪ Find the volume of a cuboid. ▪ Find the edge of a cube when given its volume.	^{US}p. 54 ^{US}p. 55, tasks1-2 ^{US}p. 59, Practice 4A, #1,5 ^{3d}p. 38 ^{3d}p. 39, tasks1-2 ^{3d}p. 43, Practice 3A, #1,5	Ex. 20, #1	4.1a
34	▪ Find an unknown dimension of a cuboid when given its volume and two dimensions or, its volume and the area of a face.	^{US}p. 55, task 3 ^{US}p. 59, Practice 4A, #2-4 ^{3d}p. 39, task 3 ^{3d}p. 43, Practice 3A, #2-4	Ex. 20, #2,3	4.1b
35	▪ Convert volume of a liquid from cm^3 to liters and vice versa. ▪ Solve multi-step word problems which involve the volume of a liquid in a rectangular tank.	^{US}p. 56, tasks 4-5 ^{3d}p. 40, tasks 4-5	Ex. 21	4.1c
36	▪ Solve multi-step word problems which involve the displacement of a liquid by a solid.	^{US}p. 57, tasks 6-7 ^{3d}p. 41, tasks 6-7	Ex. 22	4.1d
37	▪ Solve multi-step word problems which involve the rate of flow of a liquid.	^{US}p. 58, tasks 8-9 ^{3d}p. 42, tasks 8-9	Ex. 23	4.1e
38	▪ Practice.	^{US}p. 60, Practice 4B ^{US}p. 61, Practice 4C ^{3d}p. 44, Practice 3B ^{3d}p. 45, Practice 3C		4.1f

Part 1: Solving Problems — 6 sessions

Objectives

- Find the volume of a cube when given its side.
- Find the edge of a cube when given its volume.
- Find the volume of a solid made up of unit cubes.
- Find the volume of a cuboid.
- Find an unknown dimension of a cuboid when given the volume and two dimensions.
- Find an unknown dimension of a cuboid when given its volume and the area of the face perpendicular to the unknown dimension.
- Convert the volume of a liquid from cm^3 to liters and vice versa.
- Solve multi-step word problems which involve the volume of a liquid in a rectangular tank.
- Solve multi-step word problems which involve the displacement of a liquid by a solid.
- Solve multi-step word problems which involve the rate of flow of a liquid.

Materials

- Connect-a-Cubes or multilink cubes
- Unit cubes and 1000-cube from a base-10 set
- Liter measuring cup or beaker
- Graduated cylinder
- Small solids that fit in the cylinder and do not float, such as marbles, nails, metal washers

Homework

US edition	3rd edition
Workbook Exercise 20	Workbook Exercise 12
Workbook Exercise 21	Workbook Exercise 13
Workbook Exercise 22	Workbook Exercise 14
Workbook Exercise 23	Workbook Exercise 15

Notes

This unit is mostly a review of concepts learned in *Primary Mathematics 4* and *5*. Word problems here, though, will be multi-step rather than 2-step. Problems involving the rate of flow of a liquid are new here.

A cuboid is the name given here to a rectangular prism.

The volume of a cuboid is equal to its length × width × height. A formula for volume is often given as

$V = lwh$ Where V = volume, l = length, w = width, and h = height

If your students require an extensive review of basic volume concepts, refer to unit 6 of *Primary Mathematics 4B* and the accompanying Teacher's Guide for teaching points, activities, and problems.

If we know the cuboid's volume and the length of two of its sides, we can find the length of the remaining side by using division. For example, if we are given the length and width, we can find the height.

$$\text{height} = \frac{\text{Volume}}{\text{length} \times \text{width}}$$

If we know the volume and the area of one face, we can find the dimension perpendicular to that face. For example:

$$\text{height} = \frac{\text{Volume}}{\text{Area}}$$

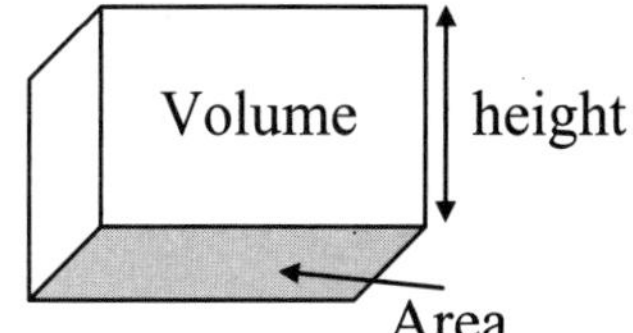

Finding a dimension of a cuboid when given the volume and the other two dimensions, or when given the volume and the area, is reviewed in this unit. If additional review is required, refer to *Primary Mathematics 5B*, unit 9 and the corresponding Teacher's Guide for teaching suggestions and problems.

For a cube, the lengths of the sides are equal so the volume is the cube of the length of a side. Students will be given a volume of a cube and asked to find the length of its side. They should know the cubes of the numbers 1, 2, 3, 4, 5 and 10, so that they can easily find the side of cubes with volumes of 1, 8, 27, 64, 125, and 1000 cubic units, and be able to use estimation and trial and error to find the side if they are given a volume which is the cube of 6, 7, 8, or 9.

Problems in this section will involve the volume of a liquid in a rectangular tank. The volume may be given in liters, and the dimensions in centimeters. Students learned in earlier levels that 1 liter = 1000 cm^3.

The volume of the water displaced by a solid is the same as the volume of the solid. The solid must be totally immersed. (This historically old method remains in use as the simplest way to measure the volume of an irregular object.)

Problems which involve converting between liters and cubic centimeters, and finding the volume of an object through displacement, were first introduced in *Primary Mathematics 5B*. If students need more review than is provided here, refer to *Primary Mathematics 5B*, unit 9, and the corresponding Teacher's Guide.

Problems involving the rate of flow of a liquid are new here. Students learned how to solve problems involving rate in *Primary Mathematics 5B*, unit 4. Rate was reviewed in *Primary Mathematics 6A* in the context of speed.

If we are given the rate of flow, such as the number of liters per minute, and the total volume, we can use rate concepts to find the time it takes for that volume to flow out of or into a tank. For example, if the rate of flow is 10 ℓ/min, then it takes one tenth of a minute for 1 liter to flow. Once we know how long it takes for one liter to flow, we can find the time for any number of liters.

Activity 4.1a **Volume**

1. Review finding the volume of a cuboid.
   - Draw a cuboid on the board and label the length, width, and height in units.
   - Ask students to find the volume in cubic units. They should remember that the volume is length × width × height.
   - Construct the cuboid with connect-a-cubes and remind them that the volume is the area of the base times the height. The area of the base gives the number of cubic units of one layer, which we can multiply by the number of layers.
   - Rotate the cuboid, have students use the area of a different side as the base, and multiply by a new height.

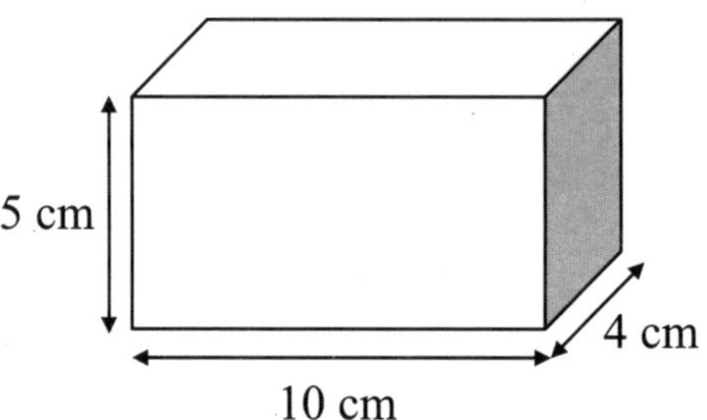

Volume = 10 cm × 4 cm × 5 cm
= 200 cm^3

Volume = length × width × height

Volume = area of base × height

2. Discuss problems which involve the volume of a cube.
   - Discuss **textbook p. 54 [3rd p. 38]**. This is a brief review for finding the volume of a cube. If necessary, you can have students construct cubes using connect-a-cubes or other multilinking cubes so that they can see that the bottom layer has 4 × 4 cubes, and adding 3 more layers to make a cube which requires 4 × 4 × 4 cubes.
   - Have students find the volume of several cubes of edges from 1 cm to 10 cm. Have students help you complete a table such as the one shown here.
   - Discuss the problem given at the top of **textbook p. 55 [3rd p. 39]**. From the table, they can see that the edge of such a cube is 9 cm. Tell students that in problems where they are given the volume of a cube, they need to find a number a for which $a \times a \times a$ is the volume. (Note: It is not correct to tell students that they need to find a number which, when multiplied by itself "3" times, gives that volume. The number is multiplied by itself twice.)

Edge of cube units	Volume cubic units
1	1
2	8
3	27
4	64
5	125
6	216
7	343
8	512
9	729
10	1000

   - Note: Students should recognize that volumes of 1, 8, 27, 64, 125, and 1000 cubic units have sides of 1, 2, 3, 4, 5, or 10 units, respectively. They can find the others by estimation and trial and error. For example, suppose they are given the volume 343 cm^3 for a cube. Since 5 × 5 × 5 is 125, the side will be greater than 5. Since 6 × 6 = 36, then 6 × 6 × 6 is less than 240 (40 × 6). 7 × 7 = 49 so 7 × 7 × 7 is about 350 (50 × 7). The most likely choice for the side of a cube with a volume of 343 cm^3 is therefore 7 cm.
   - Remove the chart from the board and have students do **problem 1, Practice 4A, textbook p. 59 [3rd Practice 3A, p. 43]** without using a table of cubes. Provide them with additional similar problems and have them solve without using a table.

3. Discuss **task 1, textbook p. 55 [3rd p. 39]**.
   - Have students suggest ways to solve this problem. Some might suggest finding the dimensions of each edge in centimeters, dividing the shape into cuboids, and finding the sum of the volumes of the cuboids. For example, the shape consists of two cuboids, one a cube with dimensions 4 cm by 4 cm by 4 cm and one a cuboid with dimensions 2 cm by 4 cm by 2 cm.
   - An easier method is to find the volume of each 2-cm cube (8 cm^3) and multiplying that by the number of cubes. There are ten 2-cm cubes, so the volume of the figure is $10 \times 8\ cm^3 = 80\ cm^3$.
   - Ask students to find the volume of the same figure if it were made of cubes of edge 3 cm, or 4 cm.
   - Ask students to find the surface area of this figure. You can have students construct the figure using connect-a-cubes, and count the number of exposed faces. There are 30 square faces, each of area 4 cm^2, so the total surface area is $30 \times 4\ cm^2 = 120\ cm^2$.

4. Have students do **problem 5, Practice 4A, textbook p. 59 [3rd Practice 3A, p. 43]**.

5. Discuss **task 2, textbook p. 55 [3rd p. 39]**.
   - Have students make suggestions for how to solve this problem.
     - You can draw the figure on the board and show how many 2-cm edges can fit along each dimension. 5 can fit along the length and along the width, and 3 along the height. So the number of cubes needed are $5 \times 5 \times 3 = 75$.
     - You can illustrate this concretely with a smaller example, such as a cuboid that is 4 units by 4 units by 6 units, using connect-a-cubes, which you can say have edges of 2 units.
   - Draw a box on the board and label the sides 15 cm, 12 cm, and 4 cm. Tell students that this is an empty box and ask them to find how many cubes of edge 2 cm can be fit into this box. To solve this, students need to determine how many blocks fit along each length. Only 7 cubes fit along the width, leaving a 1 cm gap. So the total number of cubes that can be fit into the box is $7 \times 6 \times 2 = 84$.
   - Some students may suggest finding the total volume ($15\ cm \times 12\ cm \times 4\ cm = 720\ cm^3$) and dividing by the volume of an individual 2-cm cube ($720\ cm^3 \div 8\ cm^3 = 90$). This method will only work if the lengths of all of the sides of the box are multiples of the side of the cube.

Workbook Exercise 20 [3rd Exercise 12], problem 1

Activity 4.1b **Volume**

1. Discuss finding a dimension when given the volume and two other dimensions, or the volume and an area.
   - Refer to **task 3, textbook p. 55 [3rd p. 39]**.
   - Draw the cuboid on the board.
   - Lead students to see that since we can find the volume by multiplying the area of the base by the height, we can find the height by dividing the volume by the area of the base. The area of the base is 20 cm × 12 cm = 240 cm^2.

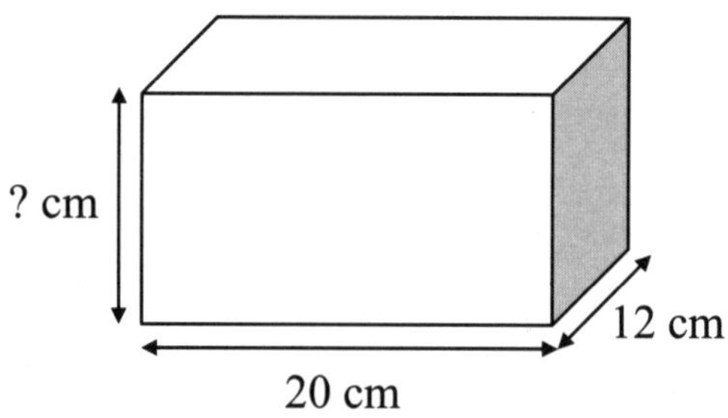

Volume = 3600 cm^3

$3600\text{ cm}^3 = 20\text{ cm} \times 12\text{ cm} \times ?\text{ cm}$
$= 240\text{ cm}^2 \times ?\text{ cm}$

$$?\text{ cm} = \frac{3600\text{ cm}^3}{240\text{ cm}^2}$$

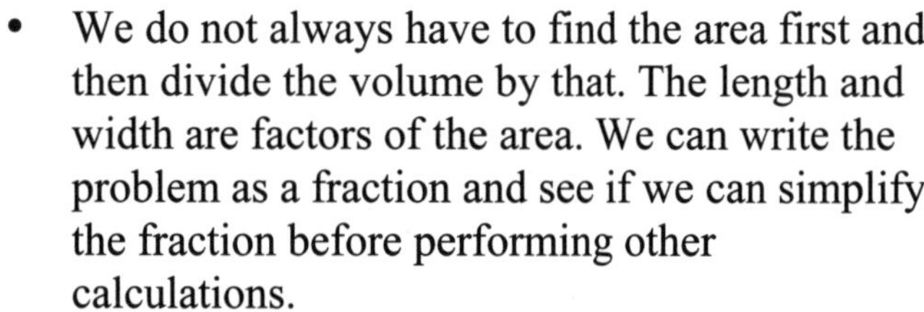

   - We do not always have to find the area first and then divide the volume by that. The length and width are factors of the area. We can write the problem as a fraction and see if we can simplify the fraction before performing other calculations.

$$\frac{360\cancel{0}}{2\cancel{0} \times 12} = \frac{\cancel{360}^{30}}{2 \times \cancel{12}_1} = \frac{\cancel{30}^{15}}{\cancel{2}_1} = 15$$

2. Discuss **problems 2-4, Practice 4A, textbook p. 59 [3rd Practice 3A, p. 43]**.
   - In problem 4, we need to first find the edge of each cube. You can discuss 2 methods for finding the edge of each cube:
     - ➢ Area of the face of each cube = 36 cm^2 ÷ 4 = 9 cm^2
       Edge of cube = 3 cm (since 3 × 3 = 9)
     - ➢ Edge of the shaded face (which is a square) = 6 cm (since 6 × 6 = 36)
       Edge of cube = 6 cm ÷ 2 = 3 cm

     The volume of each cube is therefore 3 cm × 3 cm × 3 cm = 27 cm^3.
     There are also several methods for finding the volume of the cuboid.
     - ➢ Since there are 12 cubes, and each cube has a volume of 27 cm^3, then the total volume is 12 × 27 cm^3 = 324 cm^3.
     - ➢ Since the edge of a cube is 3 cm, the edges of the cuboid are 6 cm, 9 cm, and 6 cm, so the volume is 6 cm × 9 cm × 6 cm = 324 cm^3.

Workbook Exercise 20 [3rd Exercise 12], problems 2-3

Activity 4.1c **Liters and cubic centimeters**

1. Review conversion of the volume of a liquid between cm^3 and liters.
   - Show students a centimeter cube. Tell students that the cube, if it were a container, would hold 1 cm^3 of water. 1 cm^3 has the same volume as 1 milliliter of water. Even if 1 ml of water were spread out in a teaspoon, for example, we can still say that it has a volume equivalent to 1 cm^3.
   - Ask students for the number of milliliters in a liter. There are 1000 ml in 1 ℓ. Since 1 ml = 1 cm^3, then 1000 cm^3 = 1 ℓ.
   - Show students a 1000-cube from a base-10 set, and a liter measuring cup with a liter of water in it. The water would fill up the cube, if it were a container.
   - Point out that 1000 cm^3 is not the same as 1 m^3. You can show students a meter stick and tell students that a cubic meter would have 1 m edges. 1 m = 100 cm, so 1 m × 1 m × 1 m = 100 cm × 100 cm × 100 cm = 1,000,000 cm^3. A container with a capacity of 1 m^3 would hold more water than 1 liter. It would hold 1000 liters.
   - Have students convert some values in cubic centimeters to liters and vice versa.

     1200 cm^3 = 1 ℓ 200 ml
     4 ℓ 5 ml = 4005 cm^3

2. Discuss **tasks 4-5, textbook p. 56 [3rd p. 40]**.
   - For task 5, note that the volume is left as 162 × 1000 in writing the fraction. This makes it easier to simplify the fraction. We can start simplifying by crossing out the same number of zeros in the numerator as in the denominator. Once we know what $\frac{2}{3}$ of the height is, we can find the full height with a unitary approach, or with division. (36 is $\frac{2}{3}$ of what?; $36 \div \frac{2}{3}$ = what?). The unitary approach shown below is more intuitive than division of a fraction.

$$\text{Height of water level} = \frac{162 \times \cancel{1000}^{\,2}}{9\cancel{0} \times \cancel{50}} = 36 \text{ cm}$$

$$\frac{2}{3} \longrightarrow 36 \text{ cm}$$

$$\frac{1}{3} \longrightarrow \frac{36}{2} \text{ cm}$$

$$1 \longrightarrow \frac{36}{2} \times 3 \text{ cm} = 54 \text{ cm}$$

Height of the tank = 54 cm

3. For additional practice, you can have students do **problems 1, 2, and 4, Practice 4B, textbook p. 60 [3rd Practice 3B, p. 44]** or several of the workbook problems in Exercise 21 [3rd Ex. 13] in class.

Workbook Exercise 21 [3rd Exercise 13]

Activity 4.1d **Volume and displacement**

1. Review finding the volume of a solid using displacement of water.
   - Tell students that volume does not only apply to something in the shape of a cuboid. A stone also has volume. When we find the volume of a stone as 10 cm^3, for example, that means if the stone were like clay that we could press into a cuboid, it would occupy the same space as 10 cubic centimeters.
   - Ask for suggestions on how we could find the volume of a stone. Students may remember from previous levels that if we put the stone into water, it will displace an amount of water equal to its volume. The displaced water can be measured by pouring it into a calibrated container, such as a graduated cylinder. The volume of the water displaced is the same as the volume of the stone.
   - If you have a graduated cylinder, you can demonstrate this. Fill the cylinder to a specific height with colored water, record the milliliters, add a solid to the cylinder, and record the final height. The difference in height, converted to cubic centimeters, is the volume of the solid. If feasible, you can have students determine the volume of various small solids. Note that the solid must be fully immersed. If a single solid is too small to displace enough water to measure with the graduated cylinder, have available enough of the same solid to be able to displace several milliliters of water. Students can then find the volume of a single solid. For example, if 10 metal washers displace 5 ml of water, then each washer has a volume of 0.5 cm^3.
2. Discuss **tasks 6-7, textbook p. 57 [3rd p. 41]**.
   - For task 7, note that not all the steps are given in the textbook. Students can see from the textbook how to find the increase in height (1.5cm). Ask them what else they needs so they can find the height of the new water level. To find the height of the new water level, we need to first find the original height of the water level.

     Original height $= \frac{1}{2} \times 40$ cm = 20 cm

     Height of new water level = 20 + 1.5 = 21.5 cm

3. For additional practice, you can have students do **problems 1 and 2, Practice 4B, textbook p. 61 [3rd Practice 3C, p. 45]** or several of the workbook problems in Exercise 22 [3rd Ex. 14] in class. See activity 4.1f in this guide for possible solutions to some of the practice problems.

Workbook Exercise 22 [3rd Exercise 14]

Activity 4.1e **Volume and rate of flow**

1. Review rate and discuss rate in the context of flow of water.
   - Remind students that rate involves two quantities that correspond to each other. It is usually expressed as one quantity per unit of another quantity.
   - Ask students for some examples of rate. Speed is an example of rate. If a car goes 50 miles in 1 hour, the rate (speed) of the car is 50 miles per hour.
   - Tell students that the flow of water is also a rate. For example, we can say that water fills a tank (flows into the tank) at a rate of 50 liters per minute.
   - Ask students how much water will be in the tank after 1 minute? (50 ℓ) How much will be in the tank after 2 minutes? (100 ℓ)
   - Write the problem below on the board and guide students through a solution.

> A tank is filled from a faucet. 200 liters flow into the tank in 5 minutes. How many liters will be in the tank after 8 minutes?

   - The first step is to find out how many liters will be in the tank after 1 minute. We can use an arrow diagram to show the information given; in 5 min, there will be 200 ℓ in the tank. We will put the minutes to the left of the arrow, and liters to the right, since we are going to find an unknown number of liters for a given number of minutes (8 min).

     $5 \text{ min} \longrightarrow 200\ \ell$

   - Then we find how many liters flow in 1 minute by dividing by 5.

     $1 \text{ min} \longrightarrow \frac{200}{5}\ \ell$

   - Finally, we find how many liters flow in 1 min by multiplying by 8.
     The tank will have 320 liters of water.

     $8 \text{ min} \longrightarrow \frac{200}{5} \times 8$

     $= 320\ \ell$

- Write this next problem on the board and guide students through a solution.

Using the same flow rate of 200 liters in 5 minutes, how long will it take to fill up the tank with 300 liters?

- The first step is to find how long it will take to fill the tank with 1 liter. So, when we write the relationship between minutes and liters using an arrow, we put liters first.

$$200\ \ell \longrightarrow 5 \text{ min}$$

- Then, we find out how long it takes for 1 liter to flow.

$$1\ \ell \longrightarrow \frac{5}{200} \text{ min}$$

- Now, we find the number of minutes for 300 liters.
  It will take 7.5 minutes to put 300 liters into the tank.

$$300\ \ell \longrightarrow \frac{5}{2\not{0}\not{0}} \times 3\not{0}\not{0} \text{ min} = 7.5 \text{ min}$$

- Point out that by not solving the intermediate step immediately, we can sometimes simplify the fraction, making calculations simpler.

2. Discuss **tasks 8-9, textbook p. 58 [3rd p. 42]**.
   - In task 8, we can use a unitary method to find the number of minutes for $(8 \times 5 \times 6)\ \ell$ to flow out of the tank, at the rate of 12 ℓ per minute. We see that we need to divide the volume by the rate of flow.

$$12\ \ell \longrightarrow 1 \text{ min}$$

$$1\ \ell \longrightarrow \frac{1}{12} \text{ min}$$

$$(8 \times 5 \times 6)\ \ell \longrightarrow \frac{1}{12} \times 8 \times 5 \times 6 = \frac{\not{8}^{4} \times 5 \times \not{6}^{1}}{\not{12}\ \not{2}_{1}} = 20 \text{ min}$$

   Again, the division is simplified by saving the calculation for the final step. That way, instead of finding $80 \times 50 \times 60 = 240{,}000 \text{ cm}^3$ and then dividing by 1000 to find the number of liters, we can divide $80 \times 50 \times 60$ by 1000 by simply crossing off three 0's, leaving $8 \times 5 \times 6$.
   - For task 9, students can remember from task 8 that we find the time taken by dividing liters by the rate in liters/min.

3. For additional practice, you can have students do **problem 3, textbook, Practice 4B, p. 60 [3rd Practice 3B, p. 44]**.

Workbook Exercise 23 [3rd Exercise 15]

Activity 4.1f **Practice**

1. Have students do any remaining problems from **Practice 4B and 4C, textbook pp. 60-61 [3rd Practice 3B and 3C, pp. 44-45]** and share their solutions.

Possible solutions for Practice 4C [3rd Practice 3C]:

#1. Volume of cube = $10 \times 10 \times 10 = 1000\text{ cm}^3$
Height water rises = $\frac{1000}{25 \times 25} = 1.6$ cm
New height of water = $10 + 1.6 = 11.6$ cm

#2. (a) Capacity of tank = $50 \times 50 \times 42 = 105{,}000\text{ cm}^3$
(b) Height without stone = $\frac{2}{3} \times 42\text{ cm} = 28$ cm

Height with stone = $\frac{3}{4} \times 42\text{ cm} = 31.5$ cm
Change in height = $31.5 - 28 = 3.5$ cm
Volume of stone = $50 \times 50 \times 3.5 = 8750\text{ cm}^3$

#3. Capacity of tank = $25 \times 70 \times 36 = 63{,}000\text{ cm}^3$
Volume of water needed = $63{,}000 - 4{,}500 = 58{,}500\text{ cm}^3 = 58.5\ \ell$
$9\ \ell \rightarrow 1$ min
$58.5\ \ell \rightarrow \frac{1}{9} \times 58.5 = 6.5$ min

#4. Amount of water added in 3 min = $10\ \ell \times 3 = 30\ \ell = 30{,}000\text{ cm}^3$
Volume of water that would be needed without the stone to fill the tank to 18 cm is $50 \times 40 \times 18 = 36{,}000\text{ cm}^3$
Volume of stone = $36{,}000 - 30{,}000 = 6000\text{ cm}^3$

Review

Objectives

- Review previous material.

Suggested number of sessions: 2

	Objectives	Textbook	Workbook	
Review				**2 sessions**
39-40	▪ Review		Review 3 Review 4	

Notes

Normally workbook problems are for homework, but you may want to do Review 3 or 4 in class, or select specific problems to do in class.

Possible solutions for selected problems:

Review 3

10. \$2.50 ⟶ 3 chocolate bar
    \$5 ⟶ 6 chocolate bars
    \$15 ⟶ $6 \times 3 = 18$ chocolate bars

13. 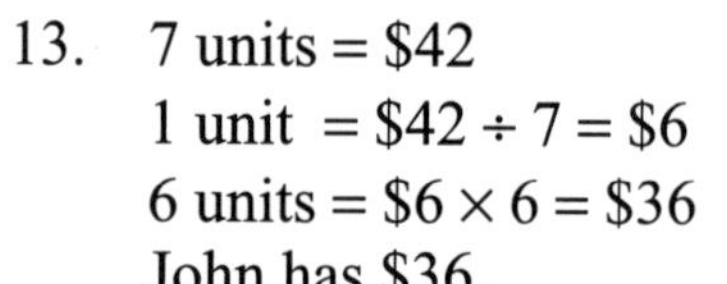
    7 units = \$42
    1 unit = $\$42 \div 7 = \$6$
    6 units = $\$6 \times 6 = \$36$
    John has \$36.

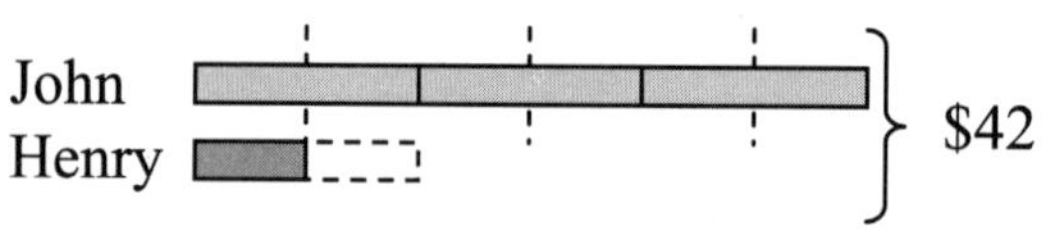

14. 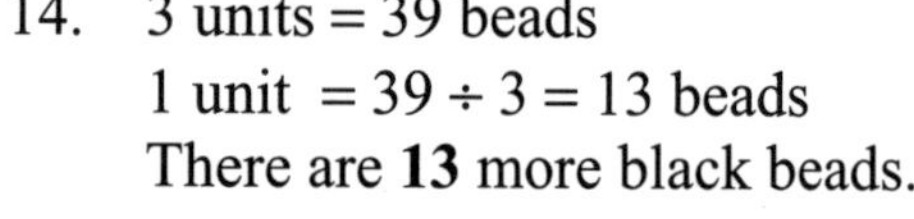
    3 units = 39 beads
    1 unit = $39 \div 3 = 13$ beads
    There are **13** more black beads.

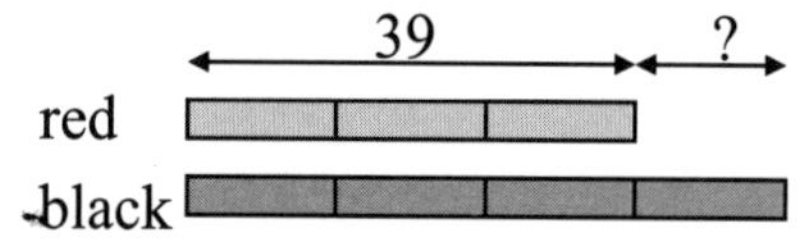

15. 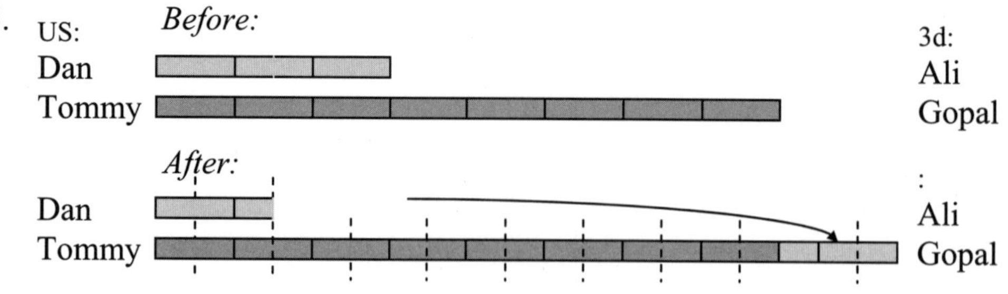

New ratio = 3 : 19

25. Money from sale of 3 watches = $3 \times \$110 = \$330$
Money from sale of 2 watches = $\$490 - \$330 = \$160$
Each of the two watches cost $\frac{1}{2} \times \$160 = \$80$.
Cost price of 5 watches = $5 \times \$80 = \$400$
Amount he made = $\$490 - \$400 = \$90$

26.
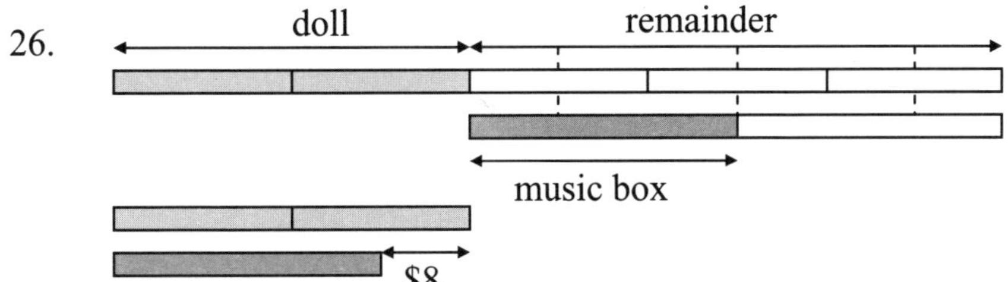

She spent half of a fifth, or one tenth of her money, more on the doll than on the box. Let $\frac{1}{10}$ of her money be 1 unit. She has 3 units left
1 unit = \$8
3 units = $\$8 \times 3 = \$24$
She had \$24 left.

Review 4

5. 48 km $\longrightarrow$ 4 ℓ
72 km $\longrightarrow \frac{4}{48} \times 72 = 6$ ℓ
The car needs 6 ℓ of gas [petrol] to travel 72 km

6. $\frac{1}{2}$ of a number is 50% of the number.
50% $\longrightarrow$ 15
10% $\longrightarrow 15 \div 5 = 3$
20% $\longrightarrow 3 \times 2 = 6$
20% of the number is 6.

Or: Half the number is 15, so the whole number is 30.
$20\% \times 30 = \frac{20}{100} \times 30 = 6$
or: 10% of 30 is 3, so 20% of 30 is twice that, or 6.

7. Cost of 1 skirt = 1 unit
4 units = \$46
2 units = $\$\frac{46}{4} \times 2 = \$23$ (Or: $\frac{1}{2} \times \$46 = \$23$)
A shirt costs \$23.

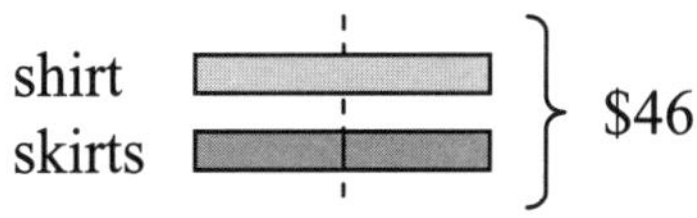

8. Total weight of 3 boys = $41.5 \times 3 = 124.5$ kg
Total weight of 2 boys = $43.7 \times 2 = 87.4$
Weight of 1 boy = $124.5 - 87.4 = 37.1$ kg

9.

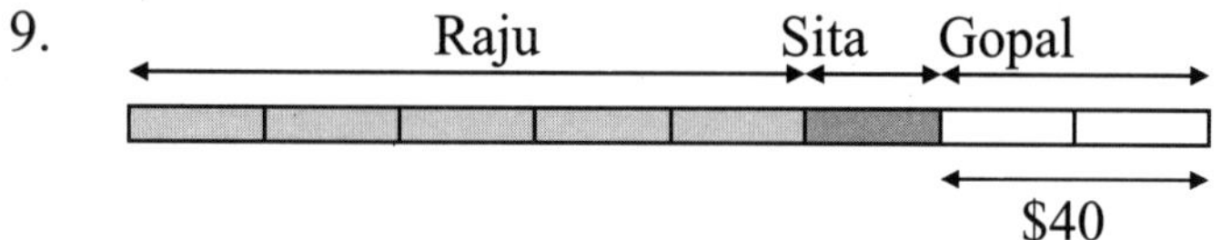

2 units = \$40
1 unit = \$20
8 units = \$20 × 8 = \$160
They had \$160 altogether.

10.

John
Peter
Peter
Mary

Mary : Peter : John = 7 : 6 : 4

11. After buying the watch, the remainder is 60%. He spent 10% of the remainder on a radio
10% of 60% = 6%
Total spent = 40% + 6% = 46%
Money left = 100% – 46% = 54%
He spent \$92, which was 46% of his money.
46% ⟶ \$92
54% ⟶ $\$\frac{92}{46} \times 54 = \$108$.
He had \$108 left.

12. Area of shaded part = area of quarter circle – half the area of the square

$$= (\frac{1}{4} \times 3.14 \times 10 \times 10) - (\frac{1}{2} \times 10 \times 10)$$

$$= 78.5 - 50 = 28.5 \text{ cm}^2$$

18.

12 km/h
16 km/h
A
B
4 km

They both traveled a half-hour.
Distance for Ryan [3rd Rajah] = 12 km/h × $\frac{1}{2}$ h = 6 km
Distance for Scott [3rd Gopal] = 16 km/h × $\frac{1}{2}$ h = 8 km
Total distance between towns = 6 + 4 + 8 = 18 km

Triangles and 4-Sided Figures

Objectives

- Review angle properties of triangles and quadrilaterals.
- Find unknown angles in problems which involve triangles and/or quadrilaterals.

Suggested number of sessions: 5

	Objectives	Textbook	Workbook	Activities
Part 1 : Finding Unknown Angles				**5 sessions**
41	▪ Review angle properties of triangles and quadrilaterals.	^{US}p. 62 ^{US}p. 63, tasks 1-3	^{US}Ex. 24	5.1a
42		^{3d}p. 46 ^{3d}p. 47, tasks 1-3	^{3d}Ex. 16	
43	▪ Find unknown angles in problems which involve triangles and quadrilaterals.	^{US}pp. 64-65, tasks 4-7 ^{3d}pp. 48-49, tasks 4-7	^{US}Ex. 25 ^{3d}Ex. 17	5.1b
44	▪ Practice	^{US}p. 66, Practice 5A ^{US}p. 67, Practice 5B		5.1c
45		^{3d}p. 50, Practice 4A ^{3d}p. 51, Practice 4B		

Part 1: Finding Unknown Angles — 6 sessions

Objectives

- Review angle properties of triangles and quadrilaterals.
- Find unknown angles in problems which involve triangles and/or quadrilaterals.

Homework

US edition	3rd edition
• Workbook Exercise 24	Workbook Exercise 16
• Workbook Exercise 25	Workbook Exercise 17

Notes

In *Primary Mathematics 5*, the students learned the following angle properties of lines, triangles, and 4-sided figures:

When a straight line passes through the vertex of two intersecting lines, the sum of adjacent angles along that straight line is 180°.

$\angle a + \angle b + \angle c = 180°$

Angles opposite each other at the intersection of two lines are equal. The opposite angles are called vertically opposite angles.

$\angle a = \angle b$

$\angle c = \angle d$

The sum of angles around a point of intersection of two or more lines is 360°.

$\angle a + \angle b + \angle c = 360°$

The sum of the three angles of a triangle is 180°. This property will be written as "$\angle$ sum of a Δ".

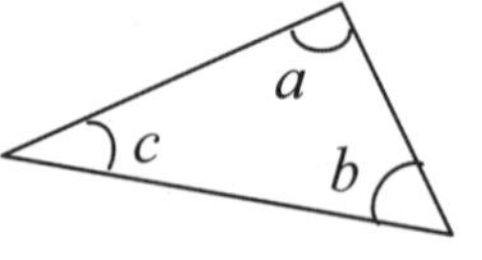

$\angle a + \angle b + \angle c = 180°$

When one angle of a triangle is a right angle, the sum of the other two angles is 90°.

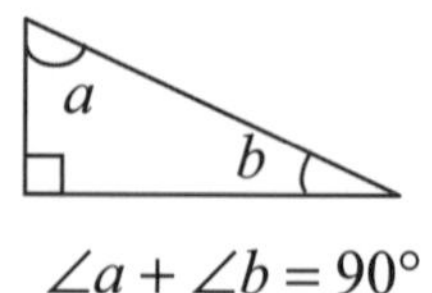

$\angle a + \angle b = 90°$

The exterior angle of a triangle is equal to the sum of the interior opposite angles. (Encourage use of this property in this section since students tend to not use it much in finding unknown angles.)

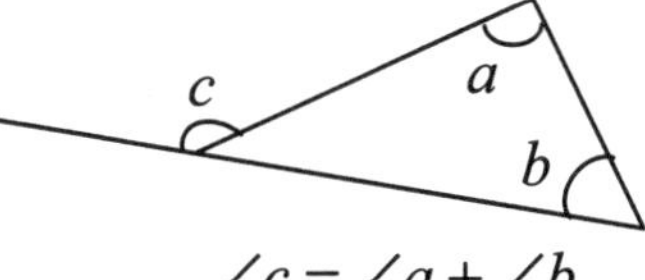

$\angle c = \angle a + \angle b$

In an isosceles triangle (a triangle with two equal sides), the angles opposite the equal sides are equal.

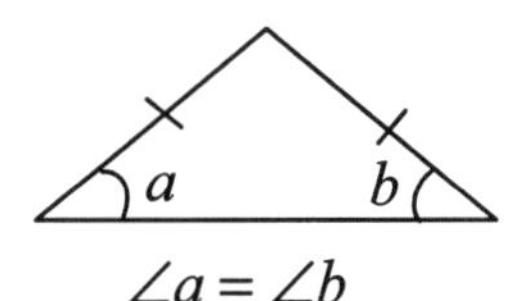

$\angle a = \angle b$

We can identify a triangle as an isosceles triangle if we know that two sides are equal or that two angles are equal.

In an equilateral triangle (a triangle with all sides equal), each angle is 60°.

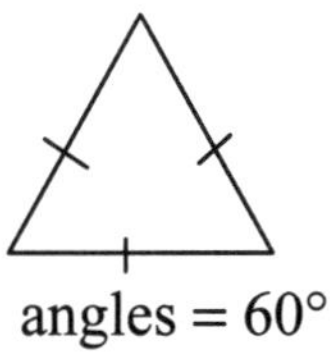

angles = 60°

We can identify a triangle as an equilateral triangle if we know that its three angles are equal, or that two angles are equal while the third angle is 60°, or that the triangle has two equal angles of 60°.

A parallelogram is a 4-sided figure with 2 pairs of parallel lines. The parallel sides are equal in length.

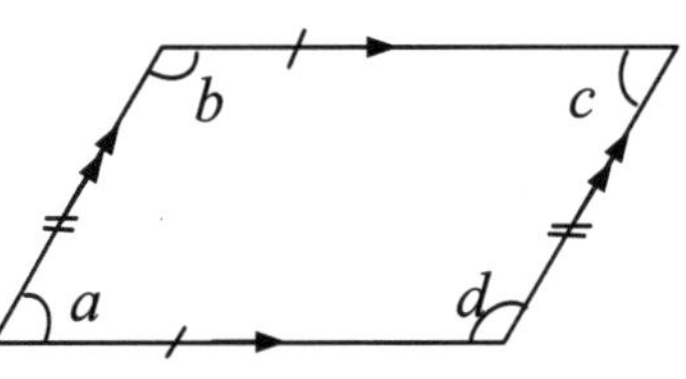

Parallel lines can be marked with arrows. Equal sides can be marked with short lines; sides marked with the same number of short lines are equal.

$\angle b = \angle d$
$\angle a = \angle c$
$\angle a + \angle b = 180°$
$\angle b + \angle c = 180°$
$\angle c + \angle d = 180°$
$\angle d + \angle a = 180°$

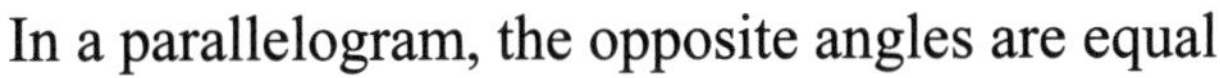

In a parallelogram, the opposite angles are equal

In a parallelogram, the sum of each pair of angles between two parallel lines is 180°

A rectangle is a parallelogram where all the angles are 90°.

A rhombus is an equilateral parallelogram (it has 4 equal sides). It has all the properties as a parallelogram. In addition, it can be divided into two isosceles triangles. The angles of the triangle opposite the equal sides of the rhombus are equal.

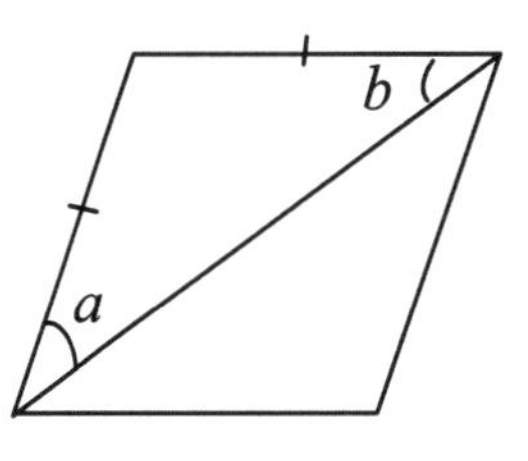

$\angle a = \angle b$

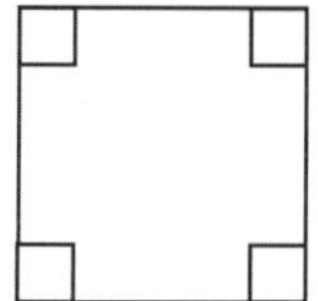

A square is a rhombus where all the angles are 90°. (It is therefore also a parallelogram and a rectangle.)

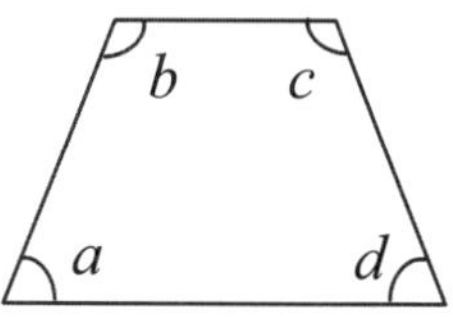

$\angle a + \angle b = 180°$
$\angle c + \angle d = 180°$

A trapezoid is a 4-sided figure with only one pair of parallel sides. The parallel sides are not equal in length. The non-parallel sides may or may not be equal in length; if they are, then the trapezoid is called an equilateral trapezoid. In the 3rd edition of *Primary Mathematics*, a trapezoid is called a trapezium (British English). The term trapezoid (American English) will be used in this guide.

In a trapezoid, the sum of each pair of angles between two parallel lines is 180°.

In this unit, students will use these properties to find unknown angles in figures composed of triangles and 4-sided figures. No new angle properties are taught here, but the figures are generally more complicated than those encountered in earlier levels. If your students need more review than is provided here, refer to *Primary Mathematics 5A*, unit 6, and *Primary Mathematics 5B*, units 6 and 7.

The illustrated figures are not drawn to scale, so students cannot use a protractor to measure the angles.

Students are not required to write down the reasons for each step of their solutions. However, they should be encouraged to give the reasons verbally.

Different steps for arriving at the value of the unknown angles are possible. Any solutions in this guide will usually show only one of the possible methods. Do not assume that a solution given here is the only "correct" solution.

Activity 5.1a **Angles**

1. Review some angle properties.
   - Refer to **textbook p. 62 [3rd p. 46]**. You can draw this diagram on the board and use it to discuss angle properties students learned in earlier levels. Ask questions such as those given in the following table. Answers are given in the right-hand column.

Name the triangle in this figure.	CDE
What is the sum of all the angles of a triangle?	180°
We say that $\angle q$ is opposite which two angles in the triangle?	∠CED and ∠EDC
What can we say about $\angle q$ in relation to these to opposite angles?	$\angle q = \angle CED + \angle EDC$
What is an equilateral triangle? (After students answer, mark each side with a short cross-line. Tell student that this means the sides are the same length.)	A triangle where all the sides and all the angles are equal.
Can we say anything about the relationship between $\angle q$ and $\angle p$?	They are on a straight line. $\angle q + \angle p = 180°$
What is a parallelogram?	It is a 4-sided figure with two pairs of parallel and equal sides.
Name the parallelogram in this figure. (Draw arrows and cross-lines to indicate parallel and equal sides. Remind students that sides marked with the same number of cross-lines are equal to each other, and sides with the same number of arrows are parallel to each other.)	ABCE
Which two angles of the parallelogram are equal? (Point out that, although it is not separately labeled, ∠AEC = ∠s.)	$\angle r = \angle q$ $\angle AEC = \angle s$
Which two angles add up to 180°?	$\angle r + \angle s = 180°$ $\angle r + \angle AEC = 180°$ $\angle q + \angle s = 180°$ $\angle q + \angle AEC = 180°$ $\angle q + \angle p = 180°$
What is a trapezoid?	A 4-sided figure with only two parallel lines.
Name the trapezoid in this figure.	ABDE
What do you know about the angles of a trapezoid?	The sum of the angles between the two parallel sides is 180°.

- Have students find the angles, and explain their reasoning.

$\angle p = 60°$	CDE is an equilateral triangle
$\angle q = 120°$	$\angle p$ and $\angle q$ are on a straight line. $\angle q = 180° - 60° = 120°$
$\angle r = 120°$	$\angle r$ and $\angle q$ are on opposite angles of the parallelogram $\angle r = \angle q = 120°$
$\angle s = 60°$	$\angle s$ and $\angle r$ are between two parallel lines. $\angle s = 180° - 120° = 60°$

2. Review some other angle properties of intersecting straight lines.
   - Draw two intersecting lines on the board and label the angles a, b, c, and d in order, clockwise.
   - Ask students to name equal angles and angles whose sum is 180°.
   - Ask students for the sum of all four angles. (360°)

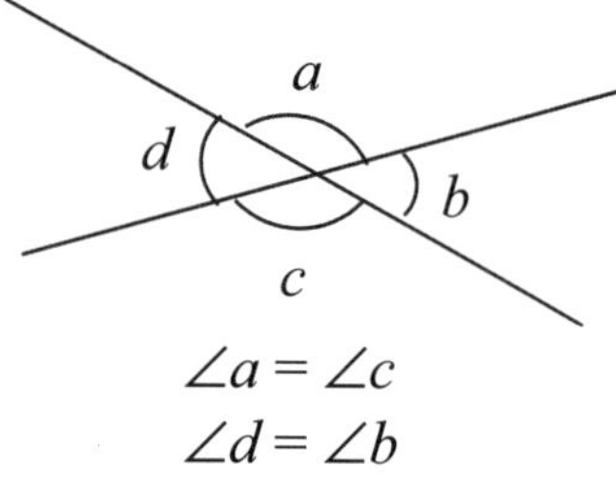

$\angle a = \angle c$
$\angle d = \angle b$

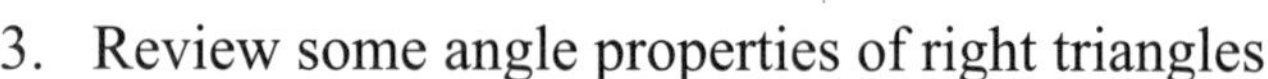

3. Review some angle properties of right triangles.
   - Draw a right triangle on the board. Mark the right angle.
   - Ask students what they know about the other two angles. Their sum is 90°. Ask students what property of triangles allows them to know this. The sum of the angles of a triangle is 180°. If one angle is 90°, then the other two must be 180° – 90°.

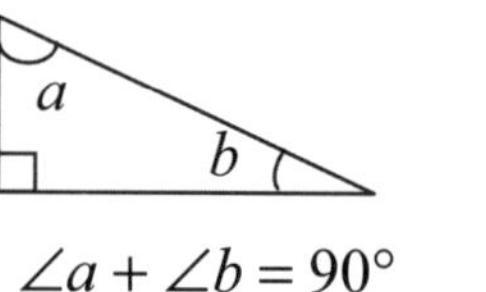

$\angle a + \angle b = 90°$

4. In *Primary Mathematics 5B*, students found that the sum of the angles of a triangle is 180° by tearing off two of the vertices of a triangle, lining them up with the third, and seeing that the three angles together formed a straight line. Students found that this was true for a variety of triangles, but this does not prove that it is true for all triangles. You can show them the following proof.
   - Remind students that a triangle is rigid, and the angles are determined when the three sides are given. (You can show this with your fingers or geostrips or strips of cardboard attached at the vertices by a brad, or a folding meter stick.) Therefore, if two triangles have the same length sides, the angles will be the same.
   - Explain that, in contrast, the angles of a parallelogram are not defined by its sides — if you construct a parallelogram from geostrips or something else where the vertices are hinged, it can "tilt" into another parallelogram with the same length sides but different angles.
   - Draw a rectangle on the board. Ask students for the sum of the angles of a rectangle. Since, by definition, each angle is 90°, then the sum of all four angles is 360°.
   - Draw a diagonal in the rectangle. Ask students if these two triangles are identical. They are, since all 3 sides of one of the triangles are the same length as those of the other triangle. So, their angles are the same. Mark the equal angles a and b. Since the diagonal forms the two angles a and b, then the sum of the angles in one triangle is 90°. Since the third angle of each triangle is also 90°, we have proven that for right triangles, the sum of the angles is 180°.

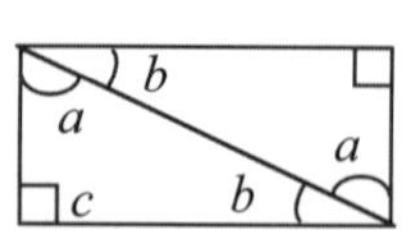

$\angle a + \angle b = 90°$
$\angle a + \angle b + \angle c = 180°$

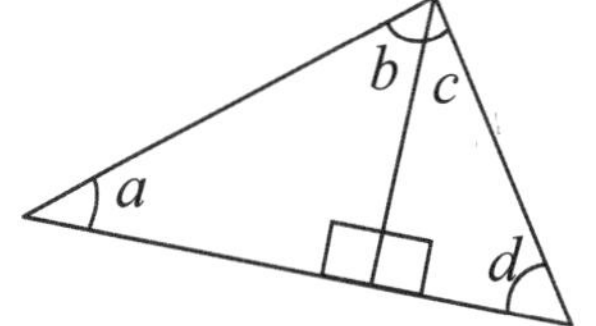

- Draw a general triangle on the board. Drop a perpendicular from the vertex to the opposite side. This gives two right triangles. Mark the angles as shown here, and write the equations to show that the sum of all the angles in a triangle is 180° (with $\angle b + \angle c$ one of the angles, and $\angle a$ and $\angle d$ the other two.

$\angle a + \angle b = 90°$
$\angle c + \angle d = 90°$
$\angle a + \angle b + \angle c + \angle d = 180°$

5. Discuss **tasks 1-3, textbook p. 63 [3rd p. 47]**.
   - Use these to review properties of isosceles triangles and rhombuses. Ask students questions about the figures.
   - For task 1, ask students what kind of triangle WXY is. It is an isosceles triangle.
     - Ask them how we know it is isosceles. We are told XW = XY. Also, the little cross-marks tell us those sides are equal.
     - Ask them for angle properties of isosceles triangles. The two angles opposite the equal sides are equal. Lead them to use these properties to find ∠XWY and ∠WYX.
       ∠XWY = (180° – 38°) ÷ 2 = 71° = ∠WYX
     - See if students can give two methods that can be used to find ∠WYZ.
       - ∠WYZ is the exterior angle of a triangle. Interior opposite angles are ∠WXY and ∠XWY.
         ∠WYZ = ∠WXY + ∠XWY = 38° + 71° = 109°
       - ∠XYW and ∠WYZ are on a straight line. We know that ∠XYW = 71°.
         ∠WYZ = 180° – 71° = 109°
   - For task 2, ask students for the properties of a trapezoid. A trapezoid is a 4-sided figure (quadrilateral) with only two parallel sides.
   - For task 3, ask students for the properties of a rhombus. A rhombus is a parallelogram with equal sides. (A square is a special type of rhombus). You can draw the figure on the board, marking the equal sides and parallel lines.
     - Can we use any properties of a parallelogram to find ∠WZY? Opposite angles are equal.
       ∠WZY = ∠WXY = 84°
     - What kind of triangle is WXY? All the sides of a rhombus are equal. That makes WXY an isosceles triangle, with XW = XY, and ∠XWY = ∠XYW.
       $\angle XWY = \frac{1}{2} \times (180° - 84°) = 48°$
6. You may want to do some of the workbook problems for Exercise 24 in class. Possible solutions are given.

Workbook Exercise 24 [3rd Exercise 16]

1.	∠XWY = 180 – 134° = 46°	(sum of ∠s on a straight line is 180°)
	∠y = ∠WXY + ∠XWY= 90° + 46° = 136°	(exterior ∠ of a Δ = sum of opposite internal ∠s)
	or:	
	∠XWY = 180 – 134° = 46°	(sum of ∠s on a straight line is 180°)
	∠WYX = 90° – 46° = 44°	(right Δ)
	∠y = 180° – 44° = 136°	(sum of ∠s on a straight line is 180°)

2. $\angle DBC = \angle EBA = 116°$ (vertically opposite $\angle$s are equal)
   $\angle d = (180° - 116°) \div 2 = 32°$ ($\angle$ sum of a Δ, isosceles Δ)

3. $\angle DBE = 90° - 50° = 40°$ (right Δ)
   $\angle b = 360° - 90° - 125° - 40° = 105°$ (sum of $\angle$s around a point is 360°)

4. $\angle BCD = 90° - 38° = 52°$ (right Δ)
   $\angle ADC = 180° - \angle BCD = 180° - 52° = 128°$ (sum of inside $\angle$s of // lines is 180°)
   $\angle x = 128° - 90° = 38°$

5. $\angle PSR = 112°$ (opposite $\angle$s of parallelogram are equal)
   $\angle m = (180° - 112°) \div 2 = 34°$ (ΔPRS is isosceles)

6. $\angle GHF = 45°$ (ΔFGH is a right isosceles Δ)
   $\angle m = 180° - \angle GHF = 180° - 45° = 135°$ (sum of $\angle$s on a straight line is 180°)

7. $\angle PQR = 90° - 20° = 70°$
   $\angle x = 180° - 70° = 110°$ (sum of inside $\angle$s of // lines is 180°)

8. $\angle PQR = 180° - 118° = 62°$ (sum of inside $\angle$s of // lines is 180°)
   $\angle y = 90° - 62° = 28°$

9. $\angle TQR = 180° - 60° = 120°$ (sum of $\angle$s on a straight line is 180°)
   $\angle TSR = \angle TQR = 120°$ (opposite $\angle$s of parallelogram are equal)
   $\angle x = 120° - 50° = 70°$

10. $\angle ADC = 180° - 104° = 76°$ (sum of $\angle$s on a straight line is 180°)
    $\angle ABC = 76°$ (opposite $\angle$s of parallelogram are equal)
    $\angle a = (180 - 76) \div 2 = 52°$ (ΔABC is isosceles Δ)

11. $\angle QRS = 180° - 112° = 68°$ (sum of $\angle$s on a straight line is 180°)
    $\angle QPS = 68°$ (opposite $\angle$s of parallelogram are equal)
    $\angle b = 180° - 46° - 68° = 66°$ ($\angle$ sum of a Δ)

12. $\angle CDE = 90° - 35° = 55°$ (right Δ)
    $\angle CBE = 55°$ (opposite $\angle$s of parallelogram are equal)
    $\angle t = 180° - 55° = 125°$ (sum of $\angle$s on a straight line is 180°)

Activity 5.1b **Find unknown angles**

1. Discuss **tasks 4-7, textbook pp. 64-65 [3rd 48-49]**.
   - Draw the figures on the board and fill in the angle measurements as they are found. Discuss the reasons that allow us to determine the angles.
   - Tell students that if they have no idea how to approach a problem, they can start by finding any angles they can find on the figure. That can lead them to seeing how to find the unknown angle. Marking equal sides with cross-marks and parallel lines with arrows can also help.
   - The boxes under the problem show that other angles need to be found before we can find the angle asked for in the problem. Other solutions may be possible.

#4. $\angle ZWV = 52°$ (isosceles ΔZWV)
$\angle ZWX = 180° - 52° = 128°$ (sum of $\angle$s on a straight line is 180°)
$\angle XYZ = 128°$ (opposite $\angle$s of parallelogram are equal)
or
$\angle VZW = 180° - (2 \times 52°) = 76°$ (isosceles Δ ZWV)
$\angle ZWX = 76° + 52° = 128°$ (exterior $\angle$ of a Δ)

#5. $\angle ACE = 45°$ (ΔACE is a right isosceles Δ)
$\angle ACD = 90° + 45° = 135°$ ($\angle ACE = 90°$)
$\angle CDA = (180° - 135°) \div 2 = 22.5°$ (isosceles ΔCDA)

#6. $\angle QRT = 62°$ (opposite $\angle$s of parallelogram are =)
$\angle QRS = 90° + 62° = 152°$
$\angle RSQ = (180° - 152°) \div 2 = 14°$ (isosceles Δ)

#7. $\angle ECB = (180° - 50°) \div 2 = 65°$ (isosceles ΔECB)
$\angle DCB = 180° - (2 \times 50°) = 80°$ (isosceles ΔDCB)
$\angle DCE = 80° - 65° = 15°$

Workbook Exercise 25 [3rd Exercise 17]
Possible solutions:

1. $\angle ADB = 18° + 26° = 44°$ (exterior $\angle$ of ΔBDC)
$\angle d = (180° - 44°) \div 2 = 68°$ (isosceles Δ)
or:
$\angle BDC = 180° - 18° - 26° = 136°$ ($\angle$ sum of a Δ)
$\angle ADB = 180° - 136° = 44°$ (sum of $\angle$s on a straight line is 180°)
$\angle d = (180° - 44°) \div 2 = 68°$ (isosceles Δ)

2. $\angle PRQ = (180° - 64°) \div 2 = 58°$ (isosceles Δ)
$\angle PRT = 180° - (2 \times 48°) = 84°$ (isosceles Δ)
$\angle t = 180° - 58° - 84° = 38°$ (sum of $\angle$s on a straight line is 180°)

3. $\angle ACB = 60°$ (equilateral Δ)
$\angle BCF = 60° + 50° = 110°$
$\angle AFC = 180° - 110° = 70°$ (sum of inside $\angle$s of // lines is 180°)
$\angle r = 180° - 70° = 110°$ (sum of $\angle$s on a straight line is 180°)

4. $\angle PML = 180° - 116° = 64°$ (sum of inside $\angle$s of // lines is 180°)
$\angle y = (180° - 64°) \div 2 = 58°$ (isosceles Δ)
or:
$\angle JPM = 180° - 116° = 64°$ (sum of $\angle$s on a straight line is 180°)
$\angle JMN = 90° - 64° = 26°$ (right Δ)
$\angle NML = 90° - 26° = 64°$
$\angle y = (180° - 64°) \div 2 = 58°$ (isosceles Δ)

5. $\angle DCF = 60°$ (equilateral Δ)
$\angle p = 180° - 90° - 60° = 30°$ (sum of $\angle$s on a straight line is 180°)

6. $\angle FEG = (180° - 38°) \div 2 = 71°$ (isosceles Δ)
   $\angle DEF = 180° - 71° = 109°$ (sum of ∠s on a straight line is 180°)
   $\angle x = 109°$ (opposite ∠s of parallelogram are equal)

7. $\angle FAD = 180° - 120° = 60°$ (sum of inside ∠s of // lines is 180°)
   $\angle BAD = 180° - 110° = 70°$ (sum of inside ∠s of // lines is 180°)
   $\angle FAB = 60° + 70° = 130°$

8. $\angle ABF = 110°$ (opposite ∠s of parallelogram are equal)
   $\angle BAF = (180° - 110°) \div 2 = 35°$ (isosceles ΔABF)
   $\angle DAB = 180° - 110° = 70°$ (sum of inside ∠s of // lines is 180°)
   $\angle DAE = 70° - 35° = 35°$

9. $\angle ADC = 32° + 90° = 122°$ (exterior ∠ of a Δ)
   $\angle DAB = 180° - 122° = 58°$ (sum of inside ∠s of // lines is 180°)

10. $\angle ABD = (180° - 40°) \div 2 = 70°$ (isosceles ΔABD)
    $\angle EAB = 70° - 40° = 30°$ (∠ABD is exterior ∠ of ΔABE)

11. $\angle DAB = (180° - 28°) \div 2 = 76°$ (isosceles Δ)
    $\angle DCB = 76°$ (opposite ∠s of parallelogram are equal)

12. $\angle DFB = 40°$ (opposite ∠s of parallelogram are equal)
    $\angle FBD = (180° - 40°) \div 2° = 70°$ (isosceles ΔBDF)
    $\angle ABF = 90° - 70° = 20°$ (∠ABD is a right ∠)
    $\angle AFB = 90° - 20° = 70°$ (right Δ)

Activity 5.1c **Find unknown angles**

1. Have students do the problems in the **textbook, pp. 66-67 [3rd pp. 50-51]** and share their solutions.
   - You may want to do some of these problems as a class activity, drawing the diagrams on the board. Remind students that if they don't immediately see how to find the requested angle, they can start by finding and marking any angles that they can find.
   - Optional: You can also draw the diagrams on the board and have students find as many other angles as they can besides those requested by the problem. For example, they could find all the angles in problem 3 of Practice 5A. They could discover some additional angle properties. For example, they can show that, in problem 1, p. 66 [3rd p. 50], ∠XPQ = ∠XYZ.

Practice 5A, p. 66 [3rd Practice 4A, p. 50]

1. $\angle a = 180° - 130° = 50°$ (sum of inside ∠s of // lines is 180°)
   $\angle b = 180° - 50° - 72° = 58°$ (∠ sum of a Δ)

2. $\angle TZS = 90° - 52° = 38°$ (right Δ)
   $\angle p = 38°$ (vertically opposite ∠s are equal)
   $\angle q = 180° - (2 \times 38°) = 104°$ (isosceles ΔXYZ)

3. $\angle ABC = 90° - 30° = 60°$ (right Δ)
   $\angle DBC = 60° - 40° = 20°$
   $\angle x = (180° - 20°) \div 2 = 80°$ (isosceles Δ)
   Optional: label the intersection of the two triangles as E. Have students find ∠ACD (50°), ∠DEC (50°), ∠AEB (50°), ∠AED and ∠BEC (130°).

4. $\angle SPQ = 82°$ (opposite ∠s of a // are equal)
   $\angle PQT = 180° - (2 \times 82°) = 16°$ (isosceles Δ)
   $\angle PQR = 180° - 82° = 98°$ (sum of inside ∠s of // lines is 180°)
   $\angle m = 98° - 16° = 82°$

5. $\angle FGH = (180° - 48°) \div 2 = 66°$ (isosceles Δ)
   $\angle EFG = 180° - 66° = 114°$ (sum of inside ∠s of // lines is 180°)
   $\angle h = 114° - 48° = 66°$ (sum of inside ∠s of // lines is 180°)

Practice 5B, p. 67 [3rd Practice 4B, p. 50]

1. Note that we are not told that IJKM is a parallelogram, so we cannot assume that $\angle p = \angle IJK$.
   $\angle JKM = 60° + 60° = 120°$ (∠JKM is exterior ∠ of equilateral ΔKLM)
   or $\angle JKM = 180° - 60° = 120°$
   $\angle p = 180° - 120° = 60°$ (sum of inside ∠s of // lines is 180°)
   $\angle q = 180° - 56° = 124°$ (sum of inside ∠s of // lines is 180°)

2. $\angle BAD = 180° - 124° = 56°$ (sum of inside ∠s of // lines is 180°)
   $\angle b = 56°$ (opposite ∠s of parallelogram)
   $\angle BAE = 180° - 90° = 90°$ (sum of inside ∠s of // lines is 180°)
   $\angle a = 90° - 56° = 34°$
   or:
   $\angle CDA = \angle ABC = 124°$ (opposite ∠s of a parallelogram)
   $\angle b = 180° - 124° = 56°$ (sum of inside ∠s of // lines is 180°)
   $\angle ADE = 180° - 124° = 56°$ (sum of ∠s on a straight line is 180°)
   $\angle a = 90° - 56° = 34°$ (right Δ)

3. $\angle x = 180° - 55° = 125°$ (sum of inside ∠s of // lines is 180°)
   $\angle VWU = 125°$ (vertically opposite ∠s are equal)
   $\angle y = (180° - 125°) \div 2 = 27.5°$ (isosceles Δ)

4. $\angle IJH = 48°$ (opposite ∠s of a parallelogram)
   $\angle JIH = (180° - 48°) \div 2 = 66°$ (isosceles Δ)
   $\angle m = 90° - 66° = 24°$

5. $\angle PRS = 45°$ (right isosceles ΔPSR)
   $\angle TRS = 45° - 20° = 25°$
   $\angle RST = 180° - (2 \times 25°) = 130°$ (isosceles ΔRST)
   $\angle w = 130° - 90° = 40°$

Review

Objectives

- Review previous material.

Suggested number of sessions: 6

	Objectives	Textbook	Workbook	Activities
Review				**6 sessions**
46-52	▪ Review	Review C Review D Review E	Review 5 Review 6 Review 7	

Possible solutions for selected problems are given here. These solutions emphasize use of bar models or a unitary approach where appropriate. Other solutions are possible.

Review C pp. 68-72 [3rd 52-56]

8. $\frac{2}{3}$ full $\rightarrow$ 60 ℓ

$\frac{1}{3}$ full $\rightarrow 60 \div 2 = 30$ ℓ

$\frac{3}{3}$ full $\rightarrow 30 \times 3 = 90$ ℓ

$\frac{3}{5} \times 90$ ℓ $= 54$ ℓ

There is 54 ℓ of water in the container when it is $\frac{3}{5}$ full.

10. John

David

John's savings : David's savings = 6 : 1

19.

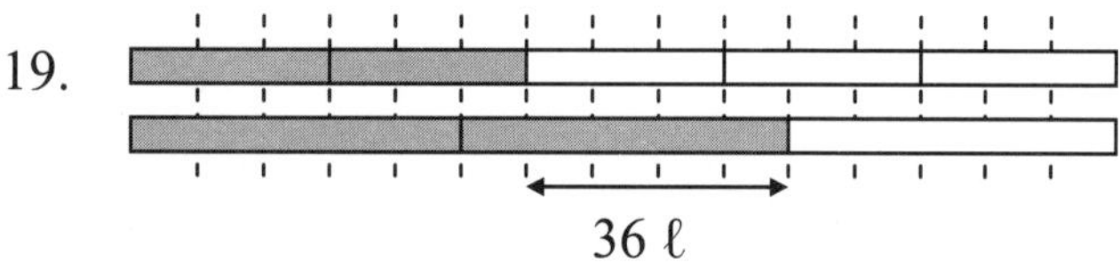

One bar shows the tank $\frac{2}{5}$ full, and the other shows it $\frac{2}{3}$ full. The lowest common multiple of 5 and 3 is 15; divide each bar into 15 to get equal units.

4 units = 36 ℓ

1 unit $= \frac{36}{4}$ ℓ

15 units $= \frac{36}{4} \times 15 = 135$ ℓ

The capacity is 135 ℓ.

20. (a) New ratio = 3 : 6 = **1 : 2**

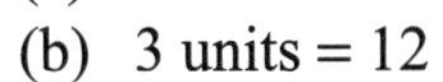

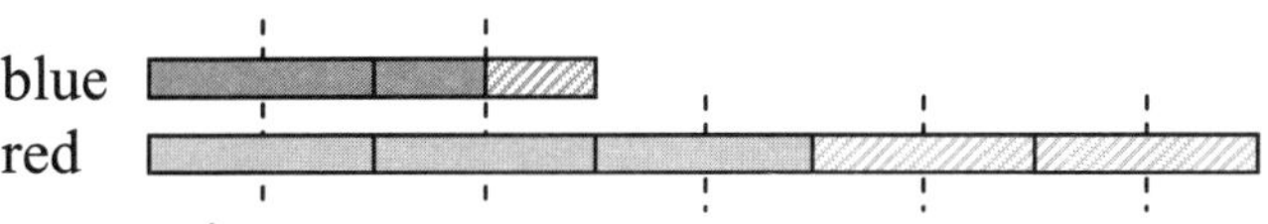

(b) 3 units = 12
1 unit = 12 ÷ 3 = 4
5 units = 4 × 5 = 20
20 beads were removed.

22. Distance for second part = 72 km/h × $\frac{1}{2}$ h = 36 km

$1\frac{1}{2}$ h $\quad$ $\frac{1}{2}$ h, 72 km/h

$\frac{1}{3}$ of the total distance = 36 km
Total distance = 36 km × 3 = 108 km
Total time = $1\frac{1}{2} + \frac{1}{2} = 2$ h
Average speed = $\frac{108 \text{ km}}{2 \text{ h}}$ = 54 km/h

23. John's time = $\frac{80 \text{ km}}{60 \text{ km/h}} = \frac{4}{3}$ h = 1 h 20 min
John left 20 min earlier, but they arrived at the same time.
David's time = 1 h 20 min – 20 min = 1 h
David's speed = 80 km/h

27. ∠QRP = 45°
∠PSR = ∠RPS
∠QRP = ∠PSR + ∠RPS = 2 × ∠RPS
∠RPS = ∠QRP ÷ 2 = 45° ÷ 2 = 22.5°

Or
∠QRP = 45°
∠PRS° = 180° – 45° = 135°
∠RPS = (180° – 135°) ÷ 2 = 22.5°

28. ∠BED = 180° - 80° = 100°
∠*x* = 180° - 100° = 80

Or
∠BCD = ∠BAD = 62°
∠ABC = 180° – ∠BAD = 180° – 62° = 118°
∠EBC = ∠ABC – ∠ABE = 118° – 80° = 38°
∠*x* = 180 – ∠EBC – ∠BCD = 180° – 38° – 62° = 80°

29. Base of Δ = 20 – 9 = 11 cm; Height of Δ = 11 cm
Area = $\frac{1}{2} \times 11 \times 11 = 60.5$ cm²

Or:

Area of rectangle = 20 cm × 11 cm = 220 cm^2
Area of unshaded triangle on the left = $\frac{1}{2}(9 \times 11) = 49.5$ cm^2
Area of unshaded triangle on the right = $\frac{1}{2}(20 \times 11) = 110$ cm^2
Area of shaded triangle = 220 cm^2 – 49.5 cm^2 – 110 cm^2 = 60.5 cm^2
Or:
Area of shaded triangle = area of half the rectangle – area of unshaded triangle on the left.

Review D pp. 73-77 [3rd 57-61]

18. She had 85% of her money left.

$15\% \longrightarrow \$60$ (music box)

$1\% \longrightarrow \$\frac{60}{15}$

$85\% \longrightarrow \$\frac{60}{15} \times 85 = \$340$

21.

apples
pears
82
240
26
82
26
240

4 units = 240 – 82 – 26 = 132

3 units = $\frac{132}{4} \times 3 = 99$

Number of apples he had at first = 99 + 82 = 181

22. 4 units = 600 – 40 = 560

1 unit = 560 ÷ 4 = 140

Alan received 140 stamps.

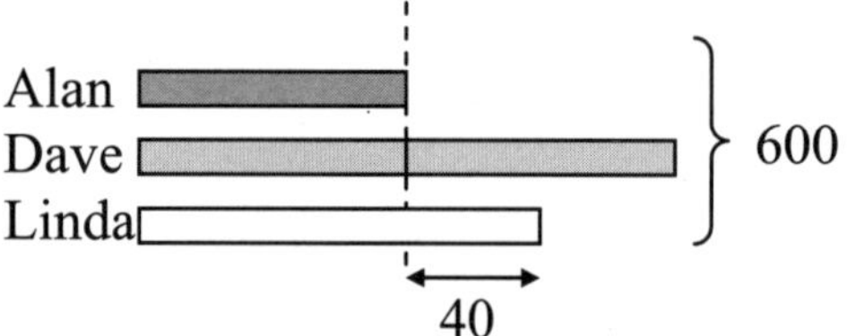

23. 7 units = \$350

3 units = $\$\frac{350}{7} \times 3 = \$150$

They spent \$150.

John
Mary
\$350

25. Number of goldfish = 4 × 20 = 80

Number of angelfish = 2 × 30 = 60

Total number of fish at first = 80 + 60 = 140

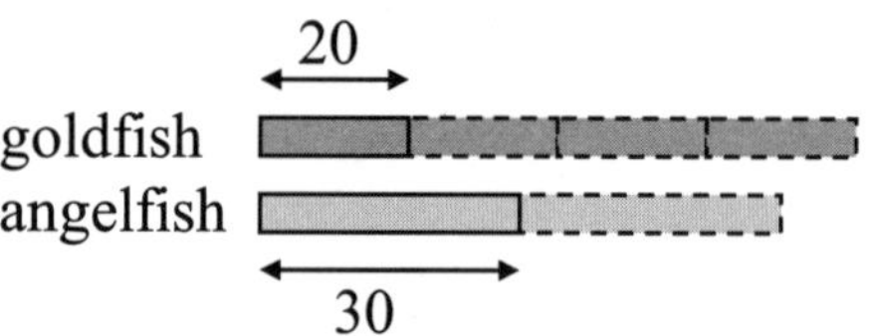

26.

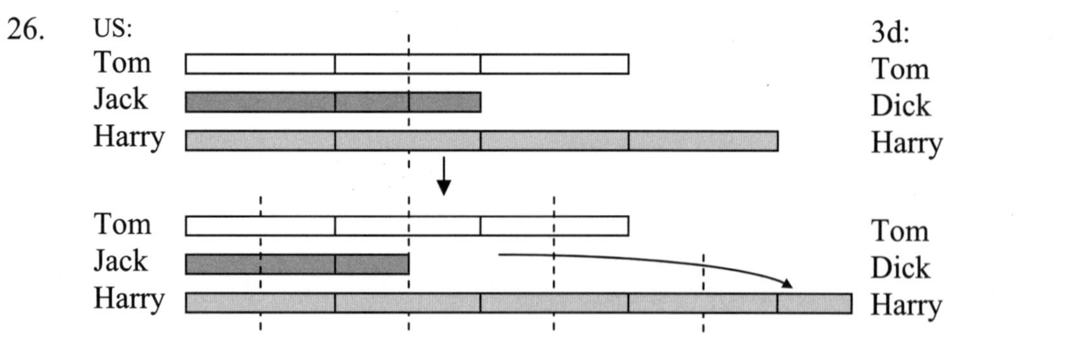

New ratio = 6 : 3 : 9 = 2 : 1 : 3

27. US: 3d:
Dan Ali
Jason Rahim
$15 $10 $15

1 unit = $15 + $10 + $15 = $40
3 units = $40 × 3 = $120
Dan [Ali] had $120 at first.

33. Volume of tank A = 36 × 8 = 288 cm^3
Volume of tank B = 5 × 3 × 12 = 180 cm^3
Volume remaining in A after filling B = 288 − 180 = 108 cm^3
Height of remaining water = $\frac{108}{36}$ = 3 cm

Review E pp. 78-82 [3rd 62-66]

19. Total weight = 60 kg × 2 = 120 kg
5 units = 120 kg
2 units = $\frac{120}{5} \times 2$ = 48 kg
The boy weighs 48 kg.

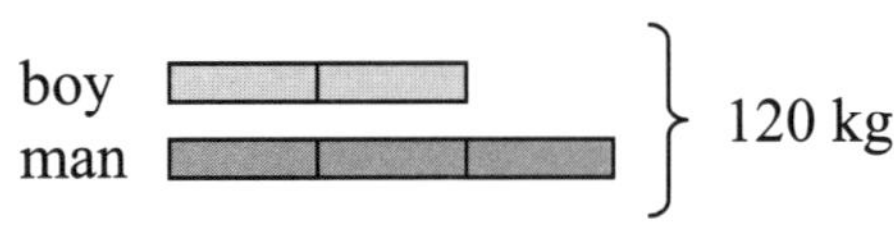

US: 3d:
Jean Devi
Lizz Siti
Marisol Meiling
$24

20. 2 units = $24
4 units = $24 × 2 = $48
Marisol [Meiling] received $48.

26.

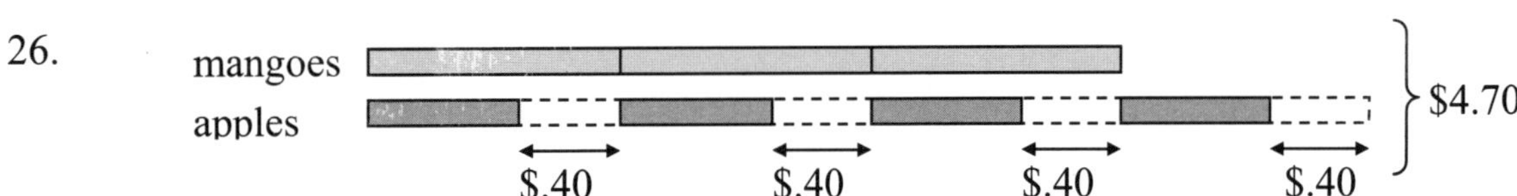

If $0.40 is added to each apple, the resulting cost would be the cost of 7 mangoes.
Cost of 7 mangoes = $4.70 + (4 × $0.40) = $6.30
Cost of 1 mango = $6.30 ÷ 7 = $0.90

27. A costs $5 more than B
B costs $2 more than C
A costs $5 + $2 = $7 more than C
Take C as the unit.
3 units = $19.50 − $9 = $10.50
1 unit = $10.50 ÷ 3 = $3.50
Book C costs $3.50.

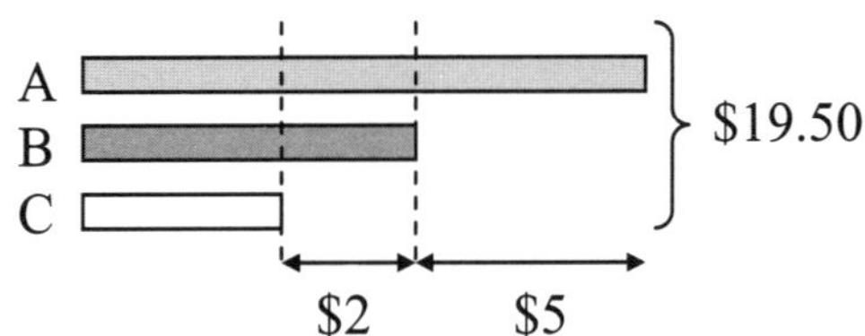

30. 1 unit of water = 4 – 2.6 = 1.4 kg

Weight of bottle = 2.6 – 1.4 = 1.2 kg

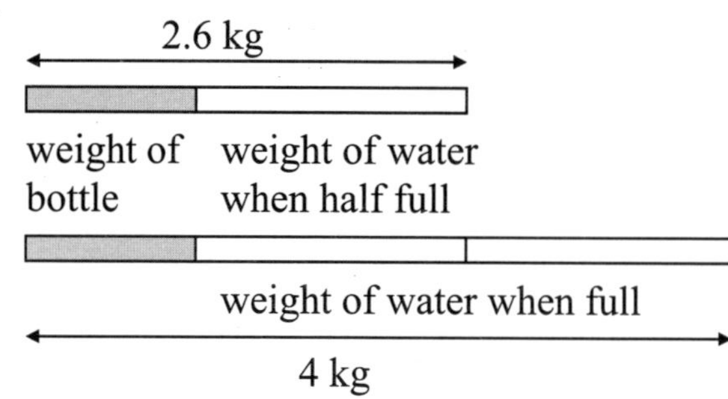

38. Height water level fell when stone was removed = $\frac{4500}{30 \times 30} = 5$ cm

Fraction of container height that water fell by $= \frac{3}{4} - \frac{5}{8} = \frac{6}{8} - \frac{5}{8} = \frac{1}{8}$

$\frac{1}{8}$ of the height = 5 cm

Height of container = 5 × 8 = 40 cm

Workbook Review 5

12. 1 unit = \$800 ÷ 8 = \$100
David's money = 3 × \$100 = \$300
John's money = 5 × \$100 = \$500
David's money after giving John \$50 = \$300 – \$50 = \$250
John's money after receiving \$50 = \$500 + \$50 = \$550
New ratio = 250 : 550 = 5 : 11

David ▭▭▭
John ▭▭▭▭▭ } \$800

13. 3 units = 60
1 unit = 60 ÷ 3 = 20
Total = 10 units = 20 × 10 = 200

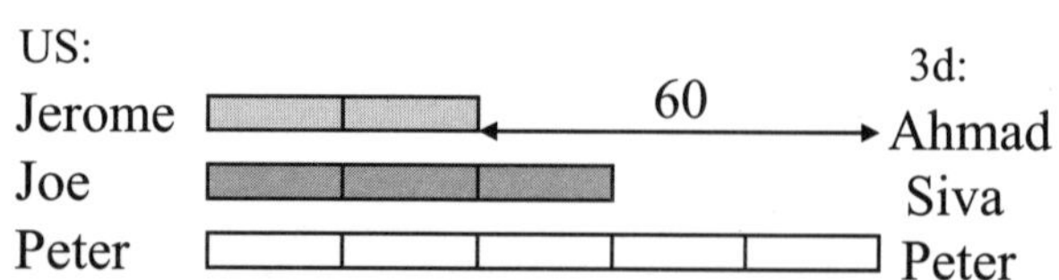

18. The shaded area is equivalent to the area of the square, since the shaded semicircle has the same area as the unshaded semicircle.
Area = 20 × 20 = 400 cm^2

23. Cost of 3 guppies = cost of 1 goldfish
Cost of 6 guppies = cost of 2 goldfish
Cost of 3 goldfish + 6 guppies = cost of 3 goldfish + 2 goldfish = cost of 5 goldfish.
If he spent $\frac{3}{5}$ of his money, then he had $\frac{2}{5}$ of his money left.

$\frac{2}{5}$ of his money = \$8

$\frac{1}{5}$ of his money = \$8 ÷ 2 = \$4

$\frac{3}{5}$ of his money = \$4 × 3 = 12

5 goldfish cost \$12
1 goldfish cost \$12 ÷ 5 = \$2.40

24. 

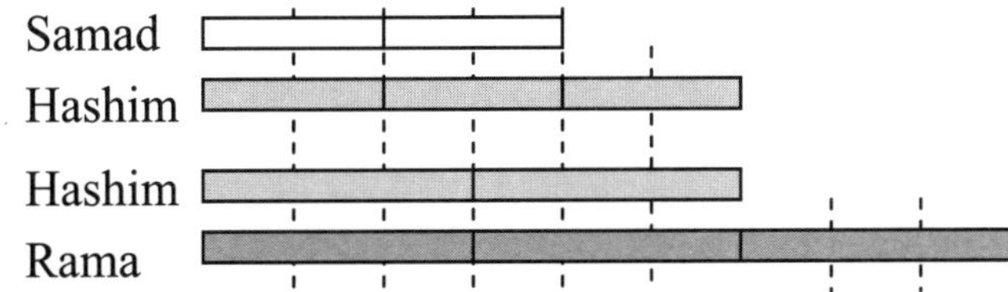

Samad : Hashim : Rama = 4 : 6 : 9

Samad had 4 units at first.
2 units = $30

1 unit $= \$\frac{30}{2} = \$15$

4 units = $15 × 4 = $60
He had $60 at first.

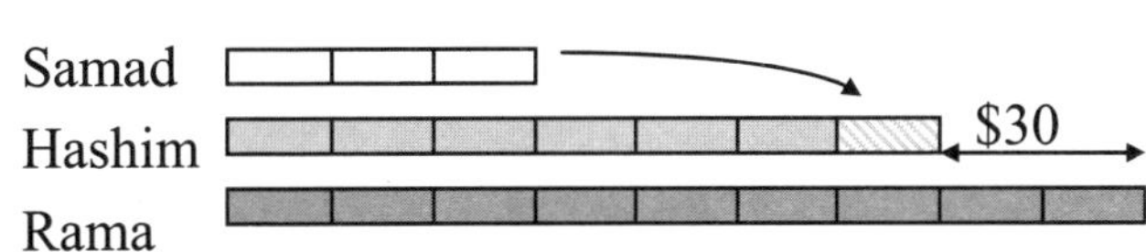

Workbook Review 6

11. The number of women is 100%. The number of men is 120%.
$120\% \longrightarrow 420$

$20\% \longrightarrow \frac{420}{120} \times 20 = 70$

There are 70 more men than women.

13. *Before*:
Total units when ratio is 1 : 2 : 6 is 1 + 2 + 6 = 9 units
9 units = $900
1 unit = $900 ÷ 9 = $100
Amount of money Henry received = 1 unit = $100
After:
Total units when ratio is 2 : 3 : 5 is 2 + 3 + 5 = 10 units
10 units = $900
1 unit = $900 ÷ 10 = $90
Amount of money Henry receives = 2 units = 2 × $90 = $180
Amount more that Henry receives = $180 – $100 = $80

14. Total units = 8
1 unit = $25
8 units = $25 × 8 = $200

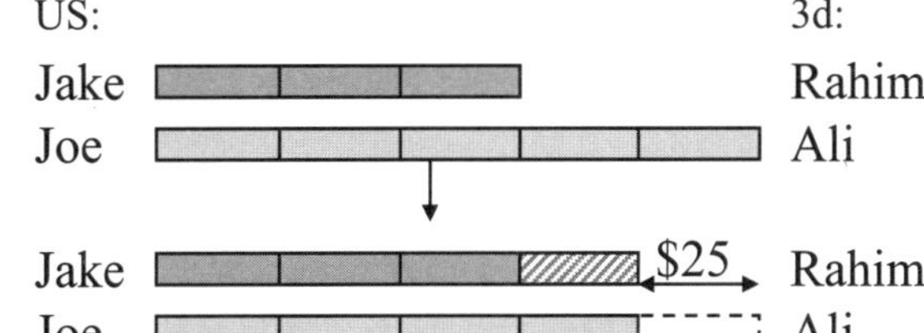

18. The base of the top triangle is 5 ft, and its height is 12 – 5 = 7 ft [3rd: cm]
The base of the side triangle is 5 ft, and its height is 8 – 5 = 3 ft [3rd: cm]
Shaded area = area of square + area of the two triangles

$$= (5 \times 5) + (\frac{1}{2} \times 5 \times 7) + (\frac{1}{2} \times 5 \times 3) = 25 + 17\frac{1}{2} + 7\frac{1}{2} = 50$$

Shaded area = 50 ft^2 [3rd: 50 cm^2]

25. 2 units = 50
1 unit = 25
6 units = 25 × 6 = 150
There were 150 boys in the club.

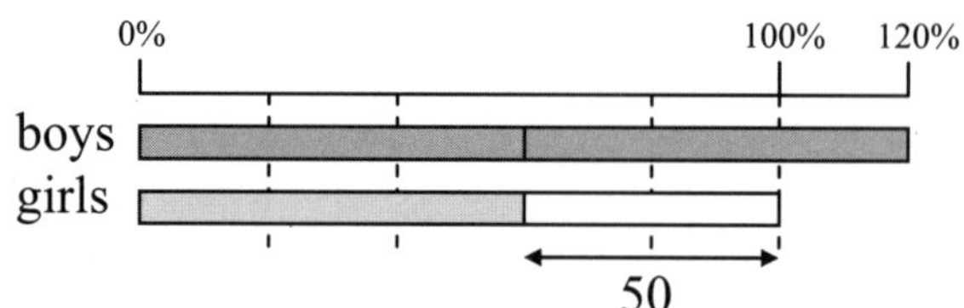

Workbook Review 7

9. 1 unit = \$50
3 units = 3 × \$50 = \$150
Peter had \$150 at first.

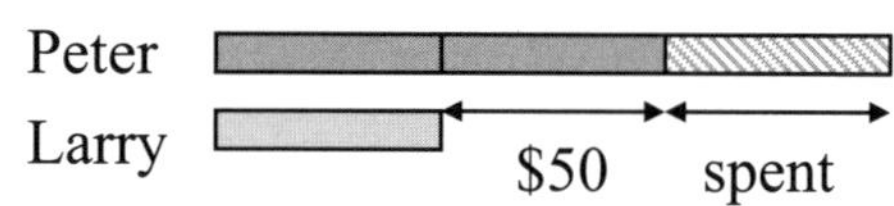

10. 5 units = 25
1 unit = 25 ÷ 5 = 5
2 units = 5 × 2 = 10

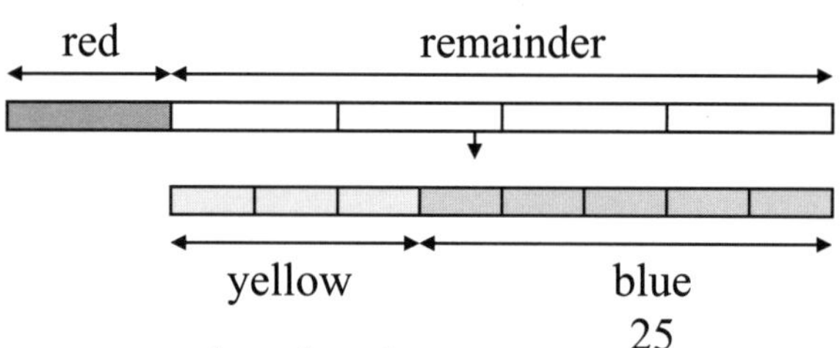

Or:

Number of blue balloons = $\frac{5}{8}$ of the remainder = $\frac{5}{8} \times \frac{4}{5} = \frac{1}{2}$

$\frac{1}{2}$ of the balloons = 25
All of the balloons = 25 × 2 = 50
Number of red balloons = $\frac{1}{5} \times 50 = 10$
There were 10 red balloons.

12. red beads : blue beads = 2 : 3 = 4 : 6
Units of red beads = 4
Units of blue and yellow = 6 + 3 = 9
Ratio of red : (blue + yellow) = 4 : 9

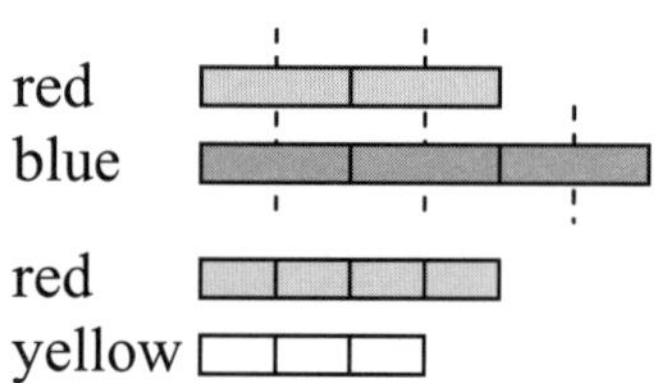

14.

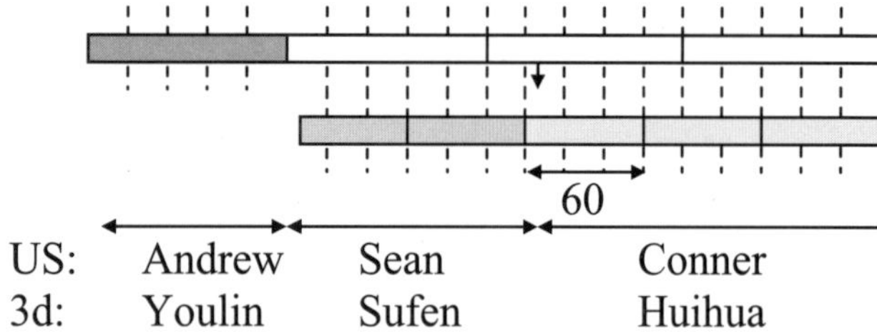

Andrew got 25% (1 large unit)
Sean + Conner = 3 units
Conner's stamps = Sean's + 60
Sean : Conner = 2 : 3, so
Difference = 1 smaller unit

1 smaller unit = 60
5 smaller units = 60 × 5 = 300= 3 larger units
1 larger unit = 300 ÷ 3 = 100
Or:
3 larger units = 5 smaller units. Lowest common multiple of 3 and 5 is 15. Divide each larger unit into 5 and each smaller unit into 3 to get equal sized units. Andrew [Youlin] has 5 units.

3 units = 60

5 units = $\frac{60}{3} \times 5 = 100$

Andrew [Youlin] received 100 stamps.

16. $\frac{3}{4}$ h, 16 km 12 km/h

A B

10:30 a.m.

Distance for first part $= 16 \text{ km/h} \times \frac{3}{4} \text{ h} = 12 \text{ km} = \frac{1}{4}$ of the distance

Distance for second part = $\frac{3}{4}$ of the total distance $= 12 \times 3 = 36$ km

Time for second part = $\frac{36 \text{ km}}{12 \text{ km/h}} = 3$ h

Total time = $3 \text{ h} + \frac{3}{4} \text{ h} = 3$ h 45 min

3 h 45 min before 10:30 a.m. is 6:45 a.m.
He left at 6:45 a.m.

25.

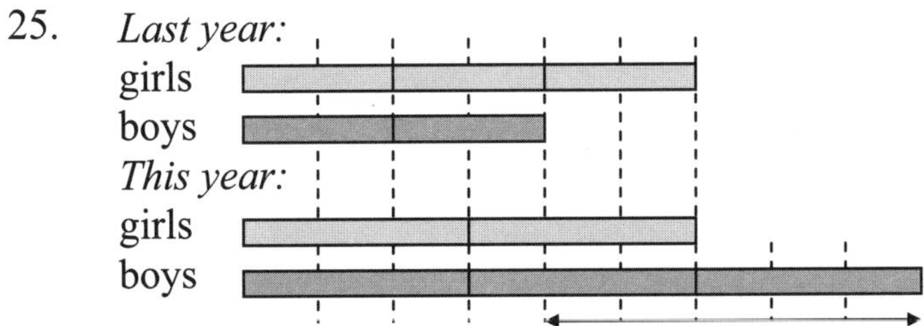

The number of girls does not change. The bar for the girls for last year has 3 units and the bar for the girls for this year has 2 units. The bars can be subdivided so that the girls have 6 equal units both years.
5 units = 15
15 units = 15 × 3 = 45
There are 45 children in the club this year.

26. Time for last third of the trip = 15 min = $\frac{1}{4}$ h

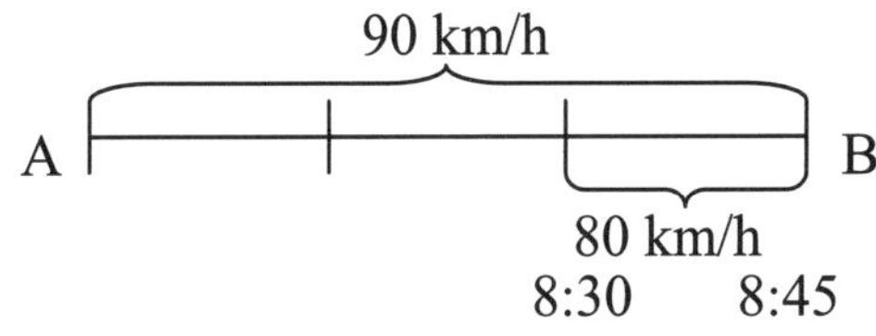

Distance for second part $= 80 \text{ km/h} \times \frac{1}{4} \text{ h} = 20$ km

Total distance = 20 km × 3 = 60 km

Total time = $\frac{60 \text{ km}}{90 \text{ km/h}} = \frac{2}{3} \text{h} = 40$ min

40 min before 8:45 a.m. = 8:05 a.m.
He left Town A at 8:05 a.m.

More Challenging Word Problems

Objectives

- Solve challenging word problems.

Suggested number of sessions: 14

	Objectives	Textbook	Activities
Part 1 : Whole Numbers and Decimals			**2 sessions**
53-54	▪ Solve challenging word problems which involve whole numbers and decimals.	US pp. 83-86, tasks 1-4 US p. 87, Practice 6A 3d pp. 67-70, tasks 1-4 3d p. 71, Practice 5A	6.1a
Unit 6 Part 2 : Fractions			**4 sessions**
55-58	▪ Solve challenging word problems which involve fractions.	US pp. 88-91, tasks 1-4 US p. 92, Practice 6B US p. 93, Practice 6C 3d pp. 72-75, tasks 1-4 3d p. 76, Practice 5B 3d p. 77, Practice 5C	6.2a
Unit 6 Part 3 : Ratio			**4 sessions**
59-62	▪ Solve challenging word problems which involve ratio.	US pp. 94-96, tasks 1-3 US p. 97, Practice 6D US p. 98, Practice 5E 3d pp. 78-80, tasks 1-3 3d p. 81, Practice 5D 3d p. 82, Practice 5E	6.3a
Unit 6 Part 4 : Percentage			**2 sessions**
63-64	▪ Solve challenging word problems which involve percentage.	US pp. 99-100, tasks 1-2 US p. 101, Practice 6F 3d pp. 83-84, tasks 1-2 3d p. 85, Practice 5F	6.4a
Unit 6 Part 5 : Speed			**2 sessions**
65-66	▪ Solve challenging word problems which involve speed.	US pp. 102-104, tasks 1-3 US p. 105, Practice 6G 3d pp. 86-88, tasks 1-3 3d p. 89, Practice 5G	6.5a

Notes

Some of the Challenging Word Problems will likely be quite hard for a moderately large number of students. You may wish to do this section after the final reviews.

You can discuss the learning tasks as a class, and then have students work on some of the practice problems in class and share their solutions. Assign other practice problems for homework, and discuss some of them the next day. You may want to assign the harder problems just to those students who have finished the easier ones.

Possible solutions to the practice problems are given in this guide. Other solutions are possible.

The problem-solving methods that have been learned throughout Primary Mathematics are a visual introduction to algebra. In finding the value for one unit in the bar diagrams, students are essentially working with unknowns and balancing linear equations.

Many of these problems can be solved algebraically, and, if you are yourself more comfortable with algebra than bar diagrams, you might think it would be easier to solve them algebraically. Though you may be tempted to show students an algebraic solution, these problems are not meant to be solved algebraically by your students. Instead, they are designed to lead your students to concentrate on finding an effective problem-solving approach. In the same way, the numbers used in these problems are selected to generally give whole number answers, focusing on the connections between different representations of numbers (fractions, decimals, percentage, ratios). As your students go on in math, they will need to carry along the skills and understanding learned here. While traditional algebra will allow them to solve problems that don't numerically "work out" as neatly, students are often given only a procedural approach to algebraic problem solving. Meanwhile, the grounding given here by the visual approach carries through to algebra, making it easier for students to set up algebraic equations correctly by first drawing at least partial models.

Students will have plenty of opportunity to solve problems algebraically as they progress; in the meantime, allow them to perfect their foundational understanding of mathematical concepts through bar diagrams at this stage. Trying to jump-start them into algebra would deprive them of some of the skills that can be used when solving the problems with bar diagrams. Consider for example problem 9 in Practice 6F:

Lauren spent 20% of her money on a dress. She spent $\frac{2}{5}$ of the remainder on a book. She had $72 left. How much money did she have at first?

In an algebraic approach, we just set up the right equation, and then solve it.
Let m = the money she had at first.
Then 0.20m = the amount spent on a dress.

$0.20m + \frac{2}{5}(m - 0.20m) + 72 = m$

$0.20m + \frac{2}{5}(0.80m) + 72 = m$

$m + 1.6m + 360 = 5m$
$360 = 2.4m$
$150 = m$
She had \$150 at first

In contrast, with a diagram approach, we can visualize the problem, and we have several options for finding the answer:

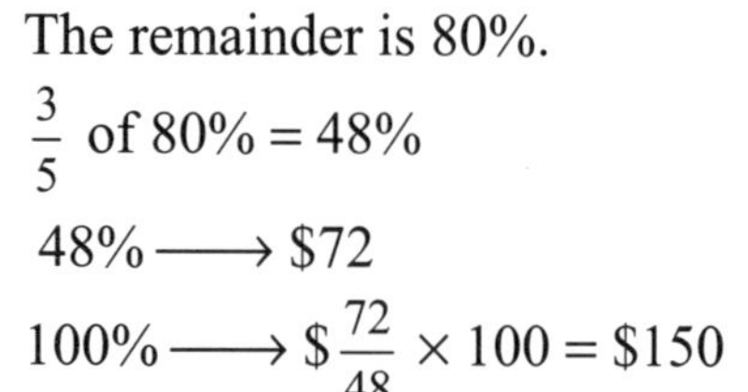

The remainder is 80%.

$\frac{3}{5}$ of 80% = 48%

$48\% \longrightarrow \$72$

$100\% \longrightarrow \$\frac{72}{48} \times 100 = \$150$

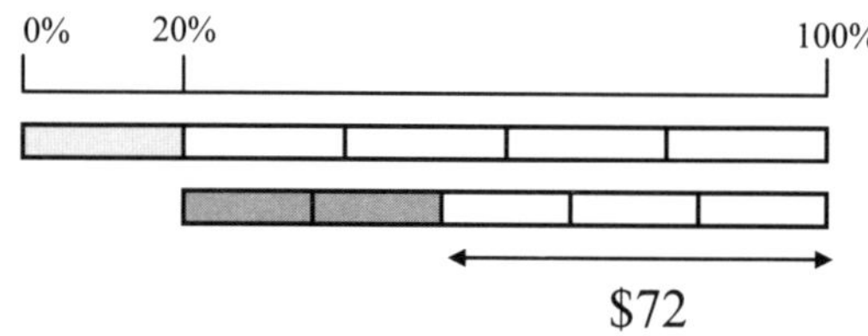

OR

3 units = \$72 (in the bottom bar diagram)

$5 \text{ units} = \$\frac{72}{3} \times 5 = \$120 = \text{remainder}$

4 parts = \$120 (in the top bar diagram)

$5 \text{ parts} = \$\frac{120}{4} \times 5 = \$150$

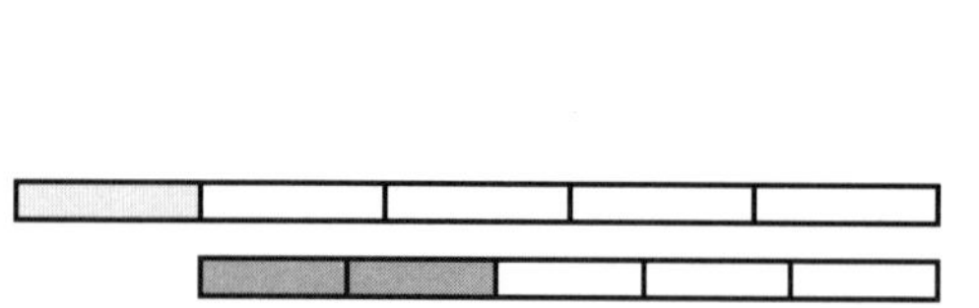

OR

Find equal units.
4 parts = 5 units
4×5 little units = 5×4 little units
Divide each part in the top bar diagram into 5 little units, and each unit in the bottom bar diagram into 4 little units. The top bar now has a total of 25 little units and the bottom bar has 20 little units, all the same size.
12 little units = \$72

$25 \text{ little units} = \$\frac{72}{12} \times 25 = 150$

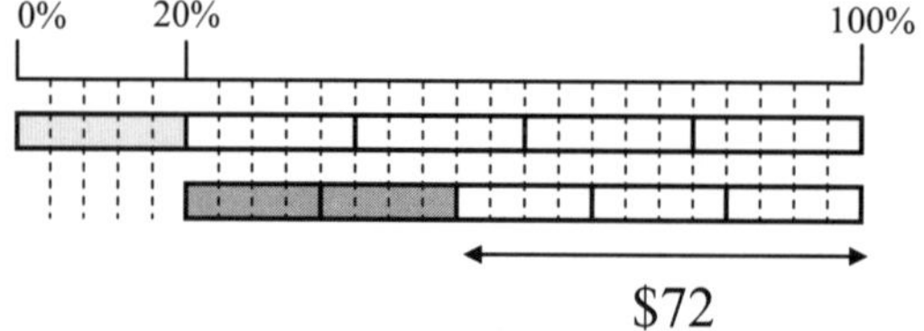

She had \$150 at first.

The diagram approach allows students to visualize the problem, and to use the relationship between fractions and percentage to solve the problem. Several different approaches are possible, one of which involves finding the lowest common multiple of 5 and 4. Students can still benefit from these skills, particularly remembering that 20% is the same as one fifth.

The algebraic solution has an advantage in that it can be used when the numbers don't work out as well, such as if the percentage were other than a recognizable fraction equivalent. But students will get plenty of problems where an algebraic approach makes more sense as they continue in math. At this stage, they should reinforce their basic understanding of number concepts by using a bar model approach with the kinds of problems they will encounter in this unit.

Part 1: Whole Numbers and Decimals — 2 sessions

Tasks 1-4, pp. 83-86 [3rd pp. 67-70]
Notes:

#1. When you show the steps on the board, you can also use an additional diagram that, instead of separating the "before" and "after" situation, has a dashed line through Gopal's unit to make 2 parts out of it. Label the second part $10, which is what he spent. Extend the line up to Raju's bar, dividing it into two parts, and label the second part $60. By superimposing the diagrams for the two situations, it can sometimes be easier to see the relationship needed to set a certain number of units equal to a value.

#2. Note that we draw the comparison model to represent Ali's money and his brother's money in the "after" situation first, since we are given a ratio between their money. Then we draw the "before" situation, relating the lengths of the bars to the "after" situation.

Alternate solution:
Since their mother gives each boy the same amount of money, the difference between their money remains unchanged.
Difference = \$130 – \$45 = \$85
1 unit "after" = \$85
Ali's money "after" = \$85 × 2 = \$170
Ali's money "before" = \$130
Amount of money given to each boy by the mother = \$170 – \$130 = \$40.

#3. We know the total difference in savings and the difference in savings per week. We use that to find the number of weeks.

Practice 6A p. 87 [3rd 5A p. 71]

1.

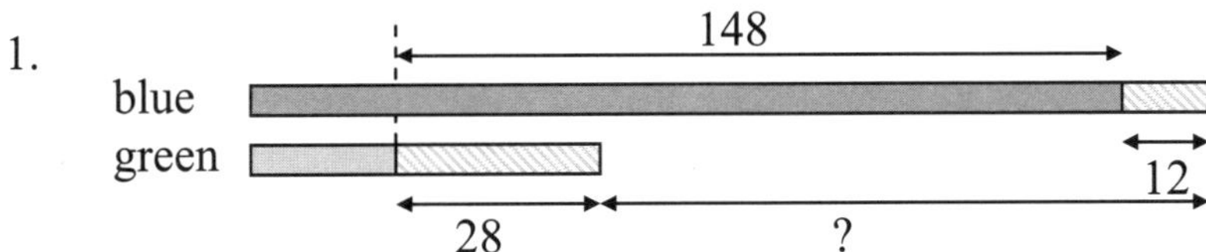

Difference = 148 – 28 + 12 = 132 beads
Or:
More green beads are added than blue beads. The difference in blue beads and green beads will be less by the amount of excess green beads added.
Excess green beads = 28 – 12 = 16
Difference = 148 – 16 = 132
There will be 132 more blue beads than green beads.

2. [3rd: meatballs are fishballs, and shrimps are prawns.]
Cost of 10 meatballs = \$1.50
Cost of 40 meatballs = \$1.50 × 4 = \$6
Cost of 600 g shrimps = \$18 – \$6 = \$12
Cost of 100 g shrimps = \$12 ÷ 6 = \$2
Cost of 1000 g shrimps = \$2 × 10 = \$20
1 kg of shrimps cost \$20.

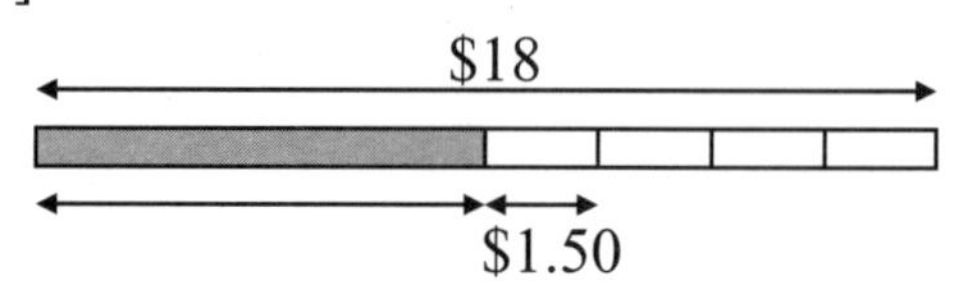

3. Number of mangoes sold = 100 – 16 = 84
3 mangoes ⟶ \$4
1 mango ⟶ $\$\frac{4}{3}$
84 mangoes ⟶ $\$\frac{4}{3} \times 84 = \$112$
Amount of money she made = \$112 – \$90 = \$22

4. 1 unit = cost of the racket
5 units = \$13.75 + (4 × \$5.50) = \$35.75
1 unit = \$35.75 ÷ 5 = \$7.15
The racket costs \$7.15
OR
1 unit = cost of birdie [3rd shuttlecock]
5 units = \$13.75 - \$5.50 = \$8.25
1 unit = \$8.25 ÷ 5 = \$1.65
Cost of the racket = \$1.65 + \$5.50 = \$7.15

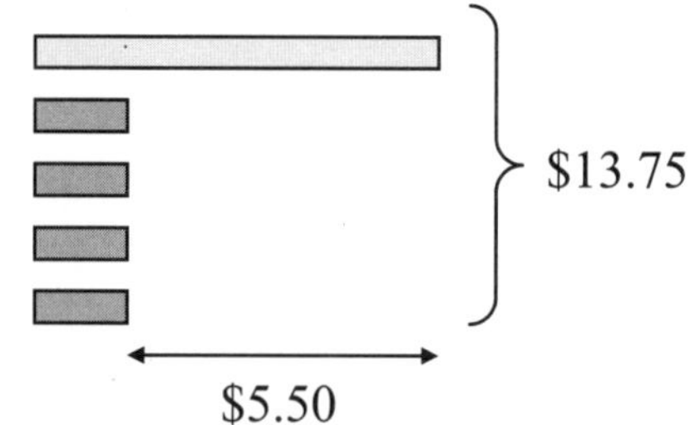

5. 1 unit = Brett's original money
3 units = Rachel's money
If we take \$9 from Rachel's money, and add \$5 to Brett's money, they have the same amount. From the diagram we see that
2 units = \$5 + \$9 = \$14
1 unit = \$14 ÷ 2 = \$7
3 units = \$7 × 3 = \$21
Rachel [Rosnah] had \$21 at first.

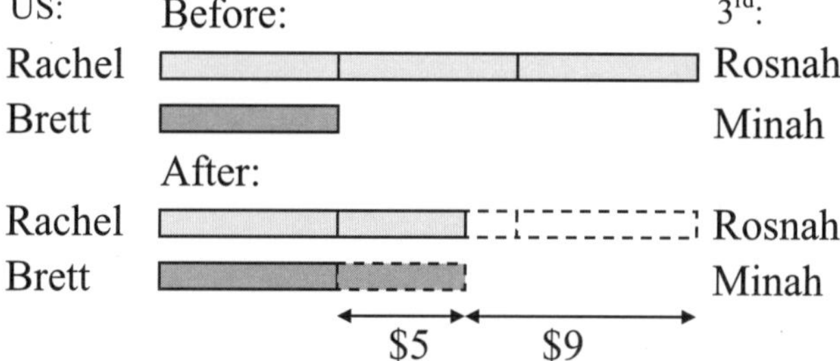

6.

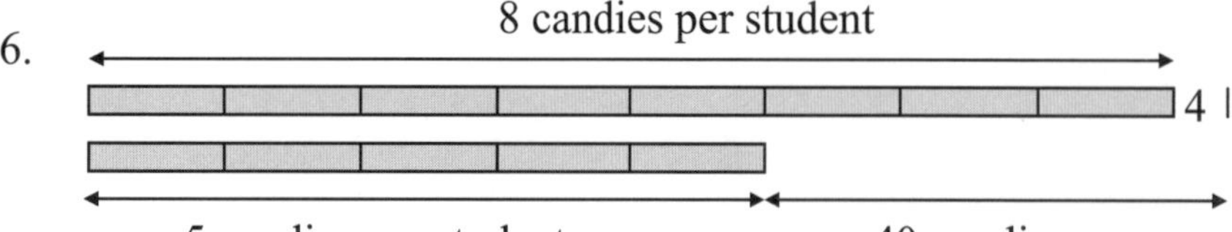

3 units = 40 – 4 = 36
1 unit = 36 ÷ 3 = 12
8 units = 8 x 12 = 96
Total candies given away = 96.
Each student gets 8 candies.
Number of students = 96 ÷ 8 = 12.

Note: We can view 1 unit as equal to each student getting 1 candy. So the value of 1 unit is the number of students in the class. If you gave each student 1 candy, that would be 1 unit.

7. 1 unit = Ricardo's money, after
Amount received
= $75 – $30 – $30 = $15
OR:
Difference remains the same.
Difference before
= $75 – $30 = $45
1 unit = $45
Amount of money received
= $45 – $30 = $15

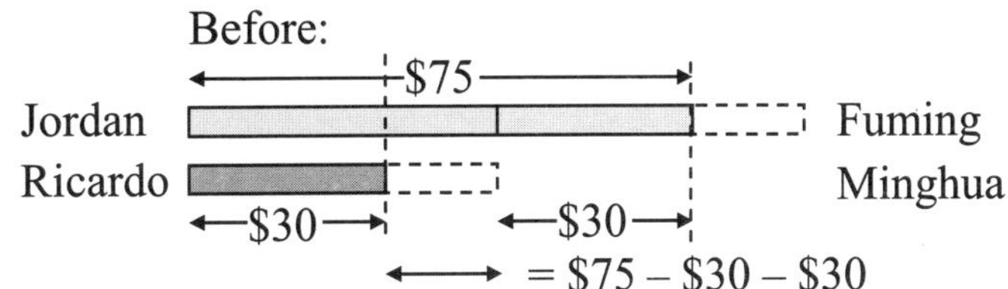

8. 1 unit = Tom's stickers, after
1 unit = 35 + (2 × 15) = 65
3 units = 65 × 3 = 195
They have 195 stickers altogether.

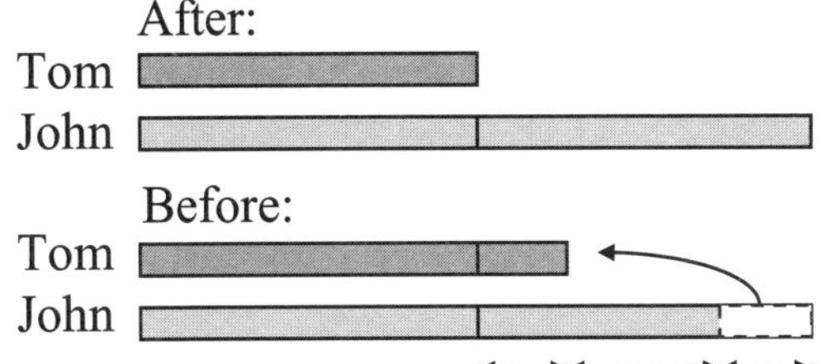

9. [3rd: Damon is Rahim and Eddie is Ahmad.]
Each day Damon spent $24 – $18 = $6 less than Eddie.
Find how many days it takes for Damon to spend $120 less than Eddie.
$120 ÷ $6 = 20
It takes 20 days for Damon to spend $120 less than Eddie, which is when Eddie had no money left. Eddie spent all his money in 20 days.
$24 × 20 = $480
They each had $480.

10.

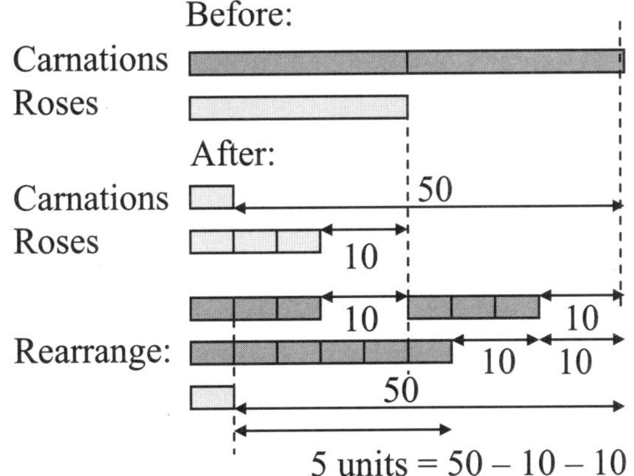

1 unit = carnations, after
Roses, before = 3 units + 10
Half of the carnations, before, also equals 3 units + 10.
You can rearrange the units to show that:
5 units = 50 – 10 – 10 = 30
1 unit = 30 ÷ 5 = 6
3 units = 6 × 3 = 18
Number of roses at first = 18 + 10 = 28

Part 2: Fractions	**4 sessions**

Tasks 1-4, pp. 88-91 [3rd 1-5, pp. 72-75]
Notes:

#1. When discussing this in class, draw the bars on the board and label the units for color to make the discussion easier to follow.
Method 1: The number of red beads is half that of yellow beads. So, if the yellow beads are 3 units, then the red beads (second bar) are $1\frac{1}{2}$ units, leaving $\frac{1}{2}$ unit for blue beads. Since there are 30 more red beads than blue beads, and 1 more unit of red beads than yellow beads, 1 unit = 30 beads.
Method 2: Divide each $\frac{1}{5}$ unit of the first bar into half, so there are now 10 units.
2 units = 30.

4. [3rd 5]. Since there are an equal number of red and blue cups left, and $\frac{2}{3}$ of the blue cups and $\frac{1}{2}$ of the blue cups are left, then $\frac{2}{3}$ of the blue cups = $\frac{1}{2}$ of the red cups.

Practice 6B p. 92 [3rd 5B p. 76]

1. Divide a bar for her total money into fourths. The remainder after spending three fourths on a dictionary is one of those fourths. She spent half of it on the calculator, so divide each fourth into half so that there her total money is now divided into 8 units.
1 unit = cost of calculator.
6 units = cost of dictionary
The dictionary costs 5 units more than the calculator.
5 units = \$30
1 unit = \$30 ÷ 5 = \$6
6 units = 6 × \$6 = \$36
The dictionary cost \$36.

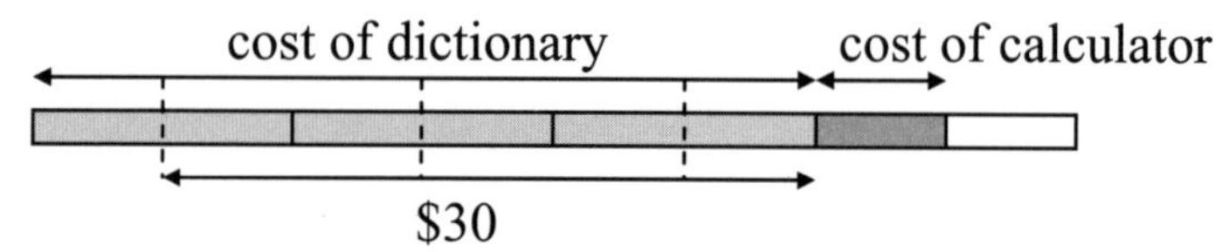

2.

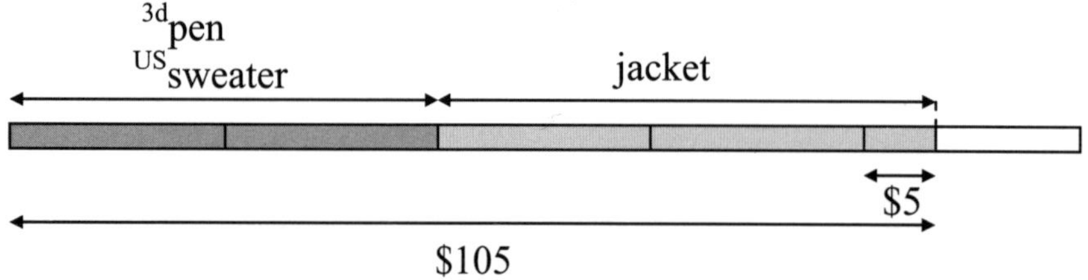

4 units = \$105 – \$5 = \$100
1 unit = \$100 ÷ 4 = \$25
Money left = \$25 – \$5 = \$20

3.

US edition, 2005 printing:

She can buy 12 pots with $\frac{2}{5}$ of her money, so 6 pots cost $\frac{1}{5}$ of her money.

Therefore, the 8 plants were bought with $\frac{2}{5}$ of her money.

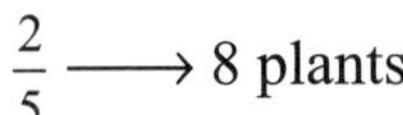

$\frac{2}{5} \longrightarrow$ 8 plants

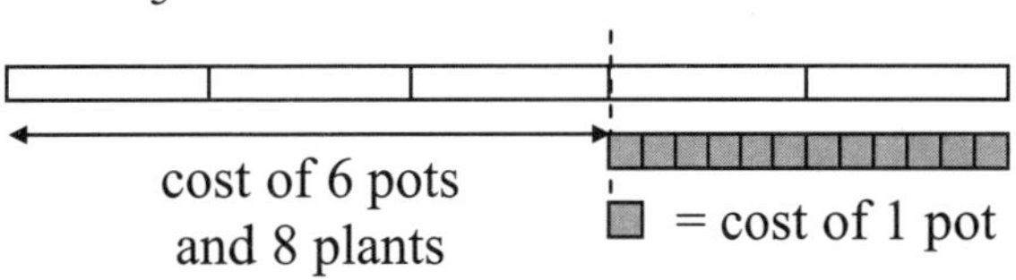

$\frac{1}{5} \longrightarrow \frac{8}{2} = 4$ plants

$1 \longrightarrow 4 \times 5 = 20$ plants.

She could buy 20 plants.

3rd edition

She can buy 6 bowls with $\frac{2}{5}$ of her money, so 3 bowls cost $\frac{1}{5}$ of her money.

Therefore, the 8 plates were bought with $\frac{2}{5}$ of her money.

$\frac{2}{5} \longrightarrow$ 8 plates

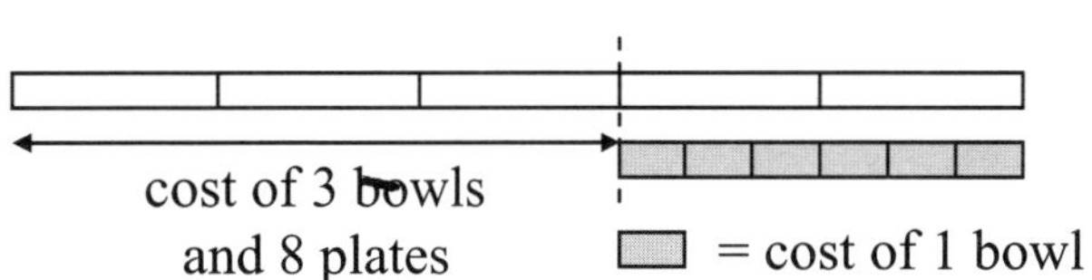

$\frac{1}{5} \longrightarrow \frac{8}{2} = 4$ plates

$1 \longrightarrow 4 \times 5 = 20$ plates.

She could buy 20 plates.

4. 1 unit = \$80

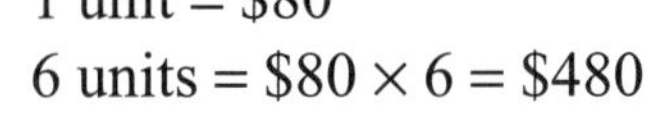

6 units = $\$80 \times 6 = \$480$

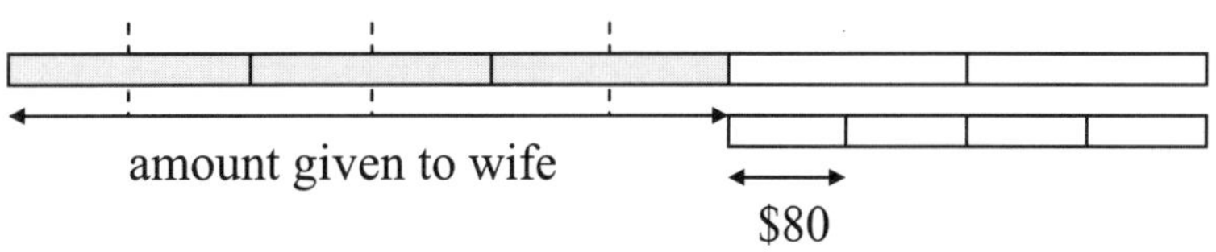

OR

Remainder is $\frac{2}{5}$ of his money. Amount given to each child = $\frac{1}{4}$ of $\frac{2}{5} = \frac{1}{10}$ of his money

$\frac{1}{10} \longrightarrow \$80$

$\frac{6}{10} \longrightarrow \$80 \times 6 = \$480$

His wife received \$480.

5. Fraction of towels that are white: $1 - \frac{2}{5} - \frac{1}{4} = \frac{20}{20} - \frac{8}{20} - \frac{5}{20} = \frac{7}{20}$

Fraction more pink than blue: $\frac{8}{20} - \frac{5}{20} = \frac{3}{20}$

$\frac{7}{20} \longrightarrow 28$

$\frac{3}{20} \longrightarrow \frac{28}{7} \times 3 = 12$

There are 12 more pink towels than blue towels.

6. Fraction spent both weeks $= \frac{1}{3} + \frac{1}{5} = \frac{5}{15} + \frac{3}{15} = \frac{8}{15}$

$\frac{8}{15}$ of his money = \$160

All of his money = $\$\frac{160}{8} \times 15 = \$300$

He had \$300 at first.

7. 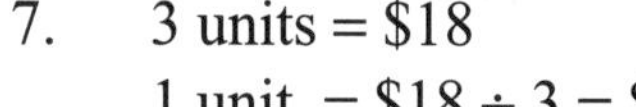
3 units = \$18
1 unit = $\$18 \div 3 = \$6$
5 units = $\$6 \times 5 = \$30$
He spent \$30 altogether.

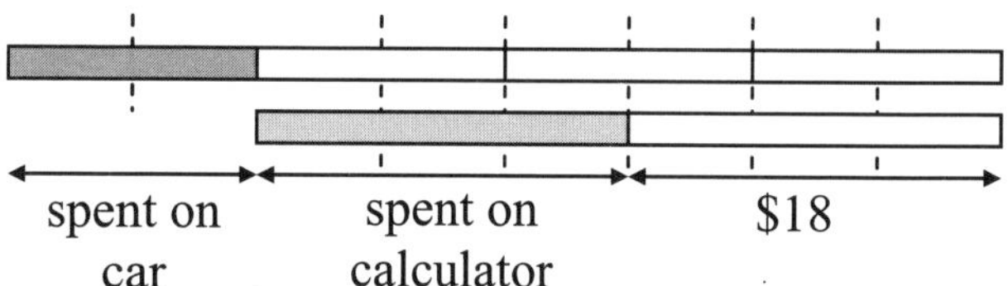

8. Cost of 1 mango = cost of 3 apples
Cost of 3 mangoes = cost of $3 \times 3 = 9$ apples.
Cost of 3 mangoes + 6 apples = cost of 9 apples + 6 apples = 15 apples

$\frac{3}{4}$ of his money $\longrightarrow$ 15 apples

$\frac{1}{4}$ of his money $\longrightarrow$ $15 \div 3 = 5$ apples

He could buy 5 more apples.

Practice 6C p. 93 [3rd 5C p. 77]

1. Fraction of beads remaining $= 1 - \frac{1}{3} - \frac{1}{9} = \frac{9}{9} - \frac{3}{9} - \frac{1}{9} = \frac{5}{9}$

Fraction of white beads = $\frac{1}{5}$ of the remainder = $\frac{1}{5} \times \frac{5}{9} = \frac{1}{9}$

$\frac{1}{9} \longrightarrow$ 25 beads

$\frac{9}{9} \longrightarrow 25 \times 9 = 225$

There were 225 beads altogether.

2. Fraction spent on watch $= \frac{3}{5} = \frac{6}{10}$

Fraction of total spent on calculator $= \frac{1}{4} \times \frac{2}{5} = \frac{1}{10}$

Difference $= \frac{6}{10} - \frac{1}{10} = \frac{5}{10} = \frac{1}{2}$

$\frac{1}{2}$ of his money = \$28

His total money = $2 \times \$28 = \$56$

3.

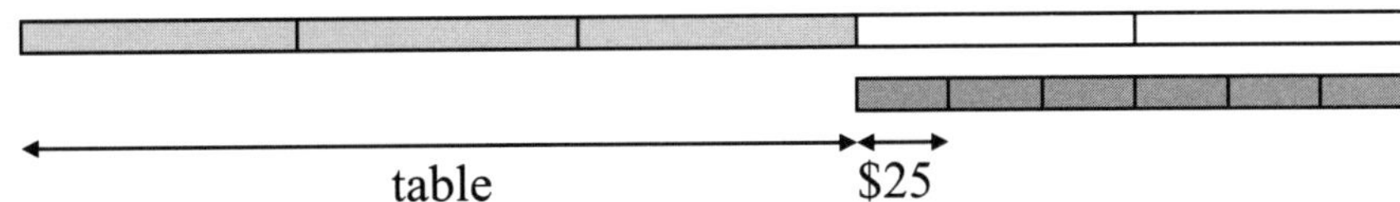

Cost of 6 chairs = $\frac{2}{5}$ of his money

Cost of 3 chairs = $\frac{1}{5}$ of his money = 3 × \$25 = \$75

$\frac{3}{5}$ of his money = \$75 × 3 = \$225

He spent \$225 on the table.

4. 6 (small) units = 54 flowers left
1 unit = 54 ÷ 6 = 9
10 units = 9 × 10 = 90
OR:

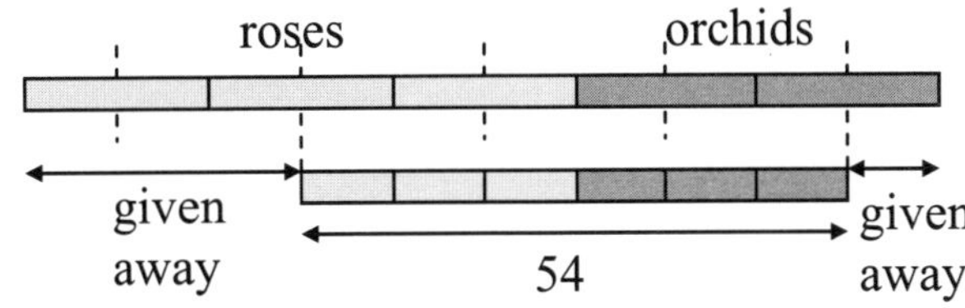

Fraction left = $1-\left(\frac{1}{2}\times\frac{3}{5}\right)-\left(\frac{1}{4}\times\frac{2}{5}\right)=1-\frac{3}{10}-\frac{1}{10}=\frac{6}{10}=\frac{3}{5}$

$\frac{3}{5}$ of the flowers = 54

$\frac{5}{5}$ of the flowers = $\frac{54}{3}$ × 5 = 90

She had 90 flowers at first.

5. [3rd: lb is kg]
3 units of oil = 3.3 – 1.5 = 1.8 lb
1 unit of oil = 1.8 ÷ 3 = 0.6 lb
Weight of bottle = 1.5 – 0.6 = 0.9 lb

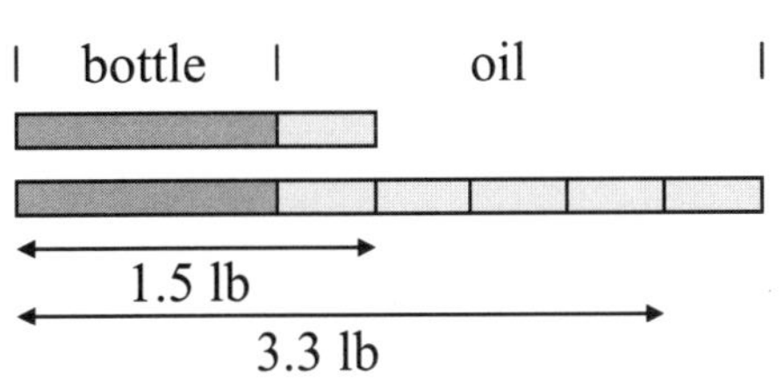

6. 10 units = \$280
1 unit = \$28
6 units = \$28 × 6 = \$168
Juanita had \$168 at first.

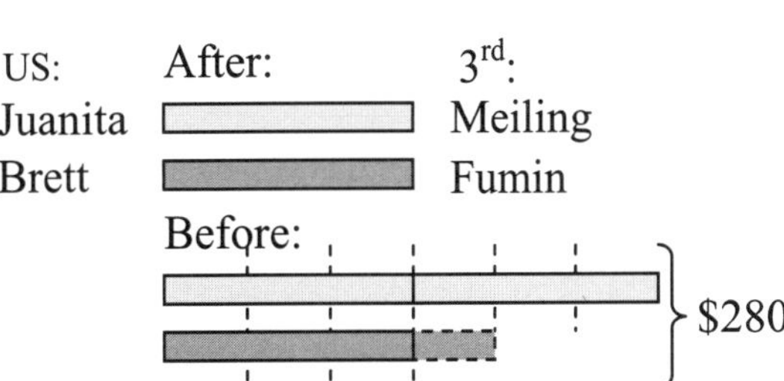

7. 1 (small) unit = cost of 1 magazine

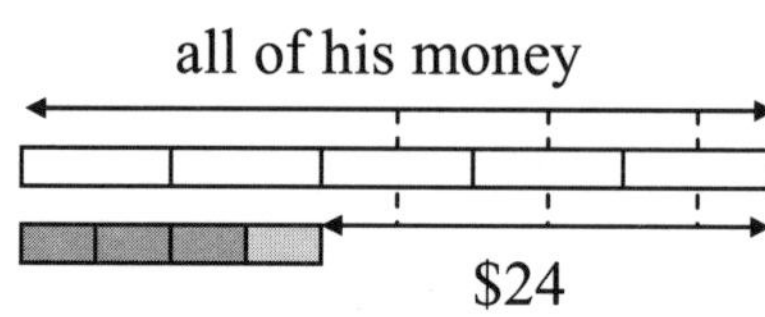

3 units = cost of 1 book

4 units = $\frac{2}{5}$ of his money

6 units = $\frac{3}{5}$ of his money = fraction of his money that he has left = $24

1 unit = $\$\frac{24}{6} = \$4$

3 units = $4 × 3 = $12

The book costs $12.

8. money she had

money spent each day

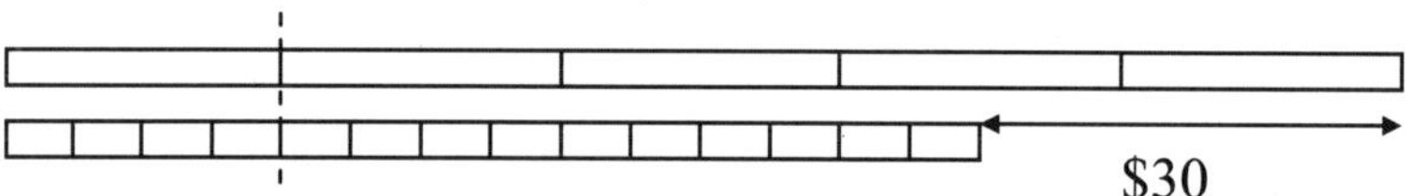

$\frac{1}{5}$ of her money = amount spent in 4 days

Divide each fifth in 4.

6 units = $30

1 unit = $30 ÷ 6 = $5

20 units = $5 × 20 = $100

She had $100 at first.

Part 3: Ratio — 4 sessions

Tasks 1-3, pp. 94-96 [3rd pp. 78-82]

Notes:

Some of the problems in this section involve one quantity given as a fraction of another. Students learned that they could interpret this as a ratio. For example, if A is $\frac{2}{5}$ of B, then the ratio of A to B is 2 : 5. Many of the strategies used to solve fraction problems by drawing bars and showing the fraction as a unit can be applied to problems involving ratio.

Practice 6D p. 97 [3rd 5D p. 81]

1. Amount of money Jane had = \$50 + \$10 = \$60
   Emma's money : Jane's money = 50 : 60 = 5 : 6
   [3rd: Suhua's money : Jane's money = 50 : 60 = 5 : 6]

2. 3 units = 18
   1 unit $= \frac{18}{3}$
   8 units $= \frac{18}{3} \times 8 = 48$
   There are 48 children altogether.

   18
   girls
   boys

3. 12 units = 360

   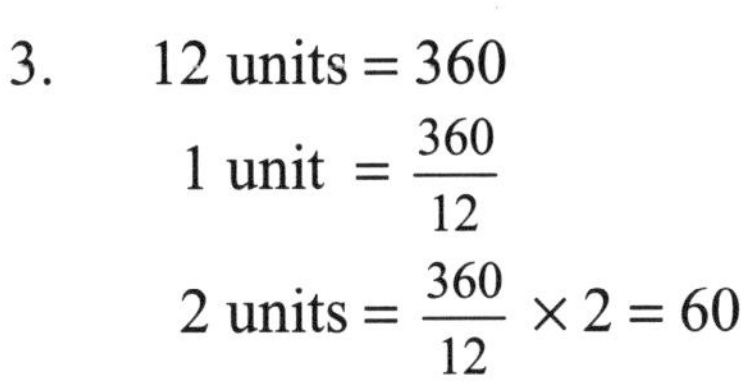

   1 unit $= \frac{360}{12}$
   2 units $= \frac{360}{12} \times 2 = 60$
   Peter has 60 more stamps than Salim.

   Peter
   Salim
   360

4. 5 units = 420 g
   14 units $= \frac{420}{5} \times 14 = 1176$ g
   The three packages weigh 1176 g.

   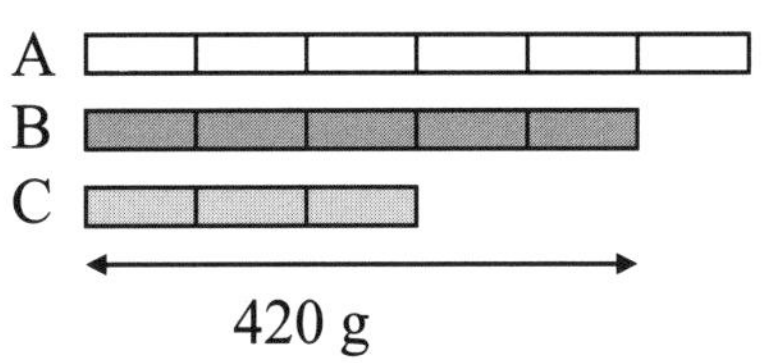

5. 12 units = 60 cm
   3 units $= \frac{60}{4} = 15$ cm
   The shortest side is 15 cm long.

   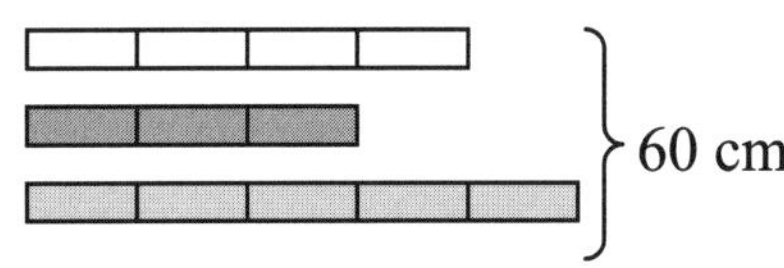

6. 2 units = \$15
   5 units $= \$\frac{15}{2} \times 5 = \$37.50$
   Rosa [Devi] received \$37.50.

   US: Mary, Sally (←\$15→), Rosa
   3rd: Mary, Sufen, Devi

7. 3 units = 18
   1 unit = $18 \div 3 = 6$

   Number of John's stamps = 5 units = $6 \times 5 = 30$
   Number of Peter's stamps = 8 units = $8 \times 6 = 48$
   Peter gives 22 stamps to John.
   New number of John's stamps = $30 + 22 = 52$
   New number of Peter's stamps = $48 - 22 = 26$
   New ratio = 52 : 26 = **2 : 1**

8. 5 units = 120
   1 unit = $120 \div 5 = 24$

   Number of men = 3 units = $24 \times 3 = 72$
   Number of women = 8 units = $24 \times 8 = 192$
   New number of men = $72 + 3 = 75$
   New number of women = $192 - 12 = 180$
   New ratio = 75 : 180 = **5 : 12**

9.

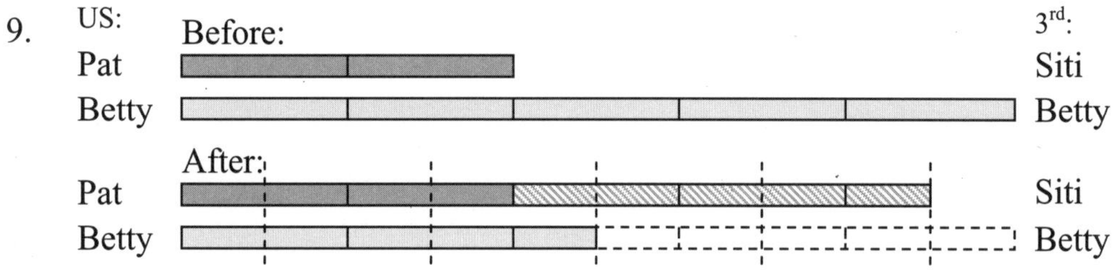

   Ratio after = **9 : 5**

10.

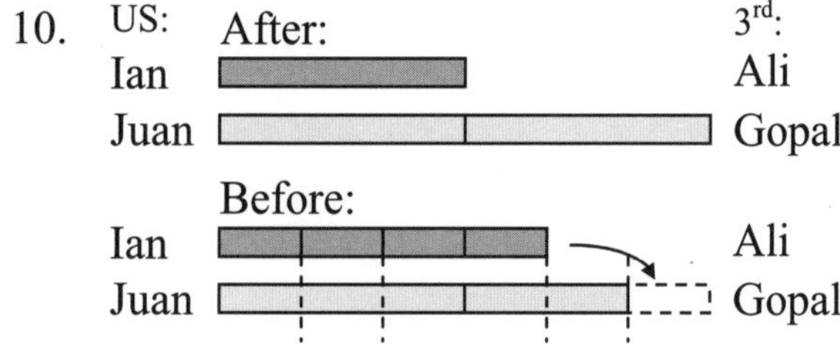

   Ratio before = **4 : 5**

Practice 6E p. 98 [3rd 5E p. 82]

1. Ratio = **6 : 1**

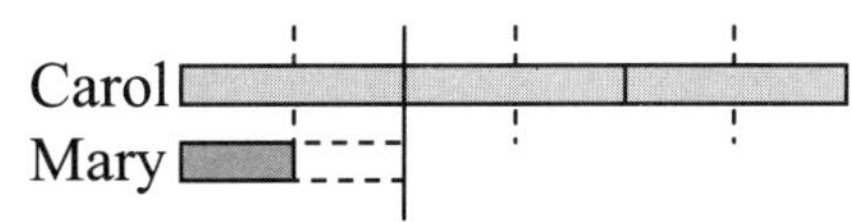

2. Ratio = **8 : 5**

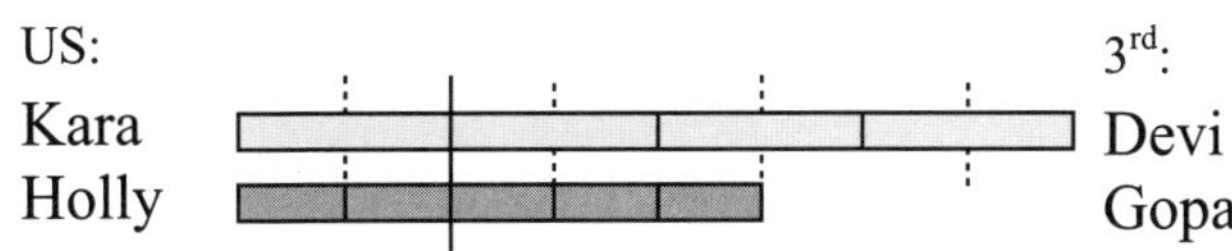

3. 7 units = \$28

   1 unit $= \$\frac{28}{7}$

   12 units $= \$\frac{28}{7} \times 12 = \$48$

   John has \$48.

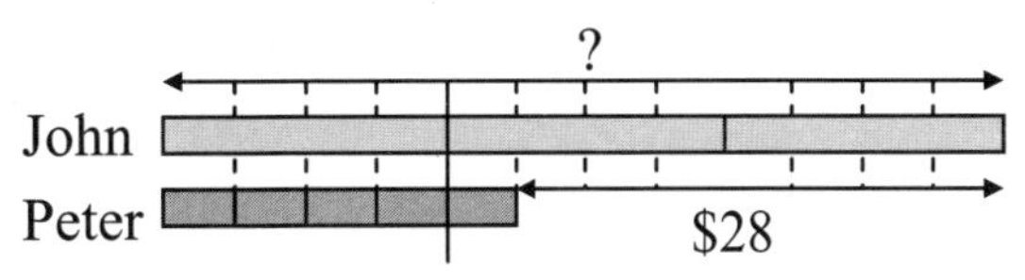

4. 4 units = 48

   10 units $= \frac{48}{4} \times 10 = 120$

   There are 120 students in the choir.

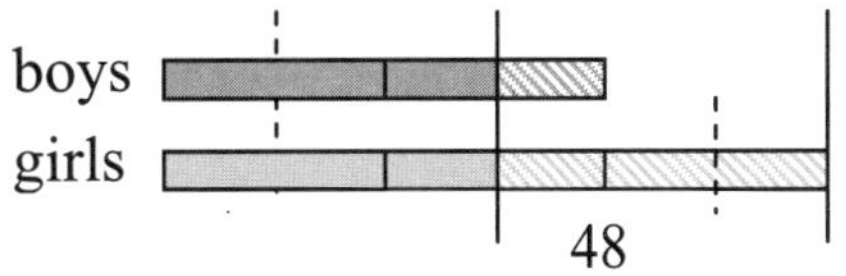

5. 3 units = \$30

   1 unit = \$10

   14 units = \$10 × 14 = \$140

   They have \$140 altogether.

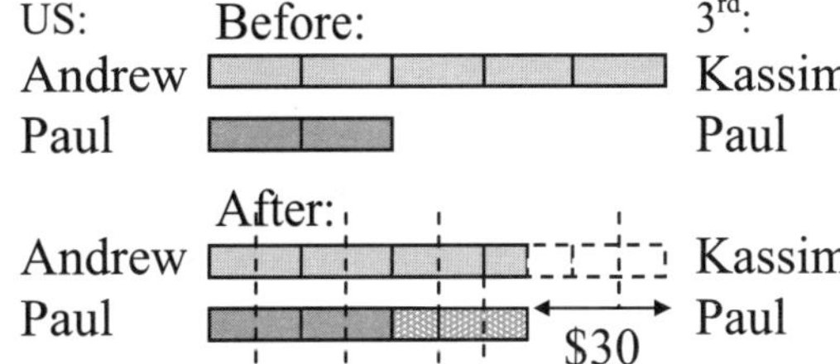

6.

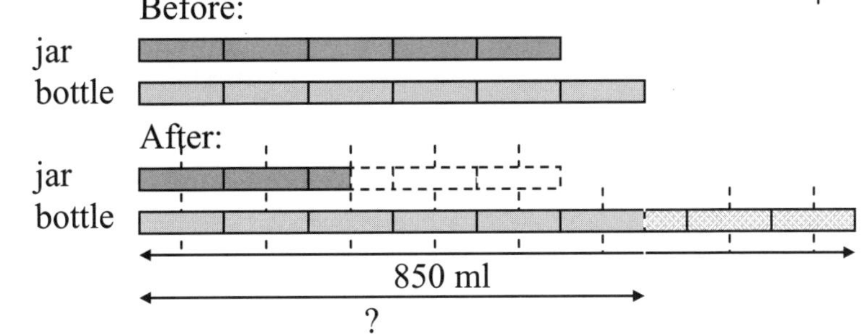

17 small units = 850 ml

1 small unit = 850 ÷ 17 = 50 ml

There were 12 small units in the bottle originally.

12 small units = 50 ml × 12 = 600 ml

The bottle had 600 ml of water.

7.

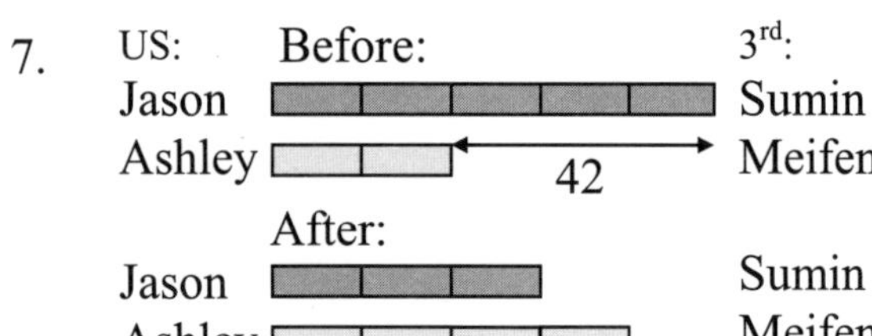

Total number of units stays 7.
Jason [Sumin] has to give Ashley [Meifen] 2 units.
3 units = 42
1 unit = 42 ÷ 3 = 14
2 units = 14 × 2 = 28
He should give her 28 stamps.

8.

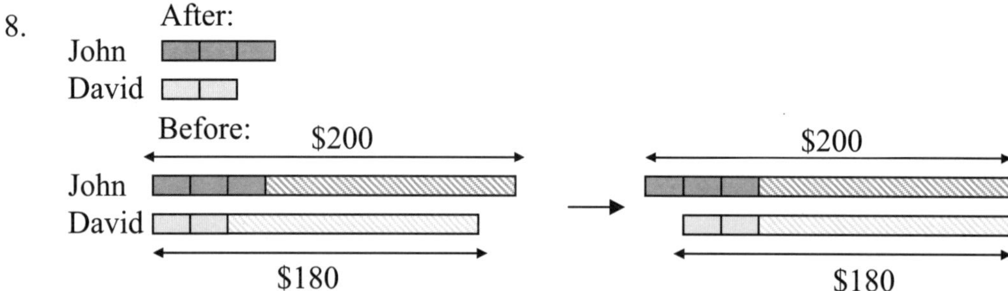

1 unit = \$200 – \$180 = \$20
2 units = \$20 × 2 = \$40
David spent \$180 – \$40 = \$140
Each spent \$140.

9.

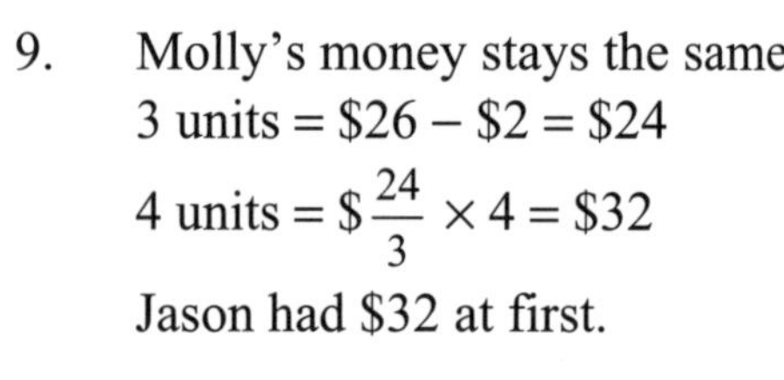

Molly's money stays the same.
3 units = \$26 – \$2 = \$24
4 units = $\$\frac{24}{3} \times 4 = \$32$
Jason had \$32 at first.

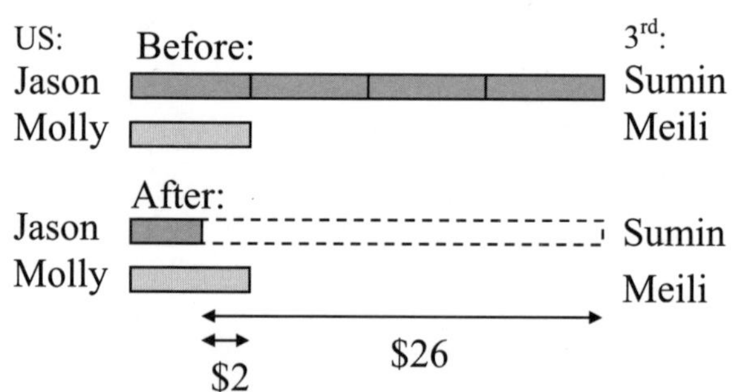

Part 4: Percentage — 2 sessions

Tasks 1-2, pp. 99-100 [3rd pp. 78-82]
Notes:

In all of these problems, it is important to establish the value to be used as the base, or 100%. In task 1 it is the cost price, and in task 2 it is the total club members.

Practice 6F p. 101 [3rd 5F p. 85]

1. The number of participants is 100%. If 60% are male, then 40% are female.

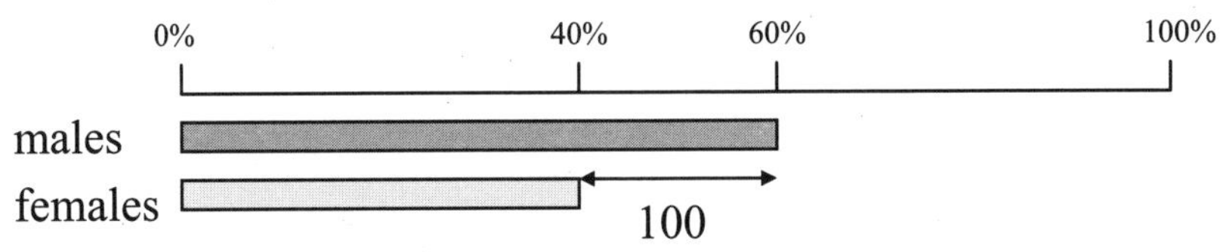

20% of the participants = 100
$20\% \longrightarrow 100$
$100\% \longrightarrow 100 \times 5 = 500$
There are 500 participants.

2.

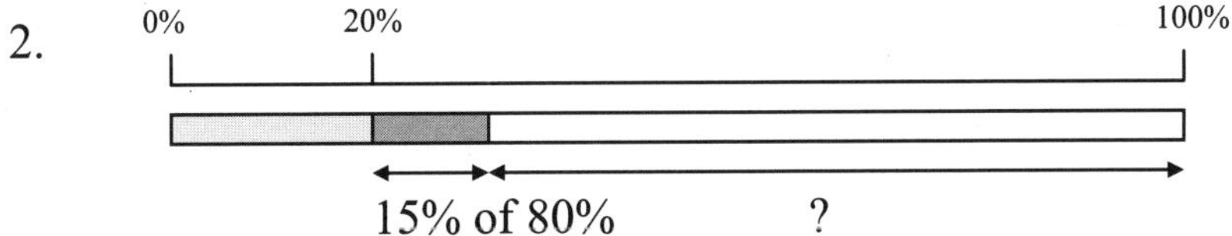

Percentage left = 85% of 80% = $\frac{85}{100} \times 80\% = 68\%$

3. The number of girls is 100%.

0% 100% 105%

girls

boys

Total number of children = 205% of the girls
5% of the girls is 2.

$5\% \longrightarrow 2$

$1\% \longrightarrow \frac{2}{5}$

$205\% \longrightarrow \frac{2}{5} \times 205 = 82$

There are 82 children altogether.

4. Amount more that she gave away = 240 – 160 = 80

   Percent more she gave away this year than last year = $\frac{80}{160} \times 100\% = 50\%$

5. Amount of stamps that Betty bought = 72 – 27 = 45

   Percent more Anne bought than Betty = $\frac{27}{45} \times 100\% = 60\%$

6. [3rd: U.S. stamps are Malaysian stamps.)

   Number of Singapore stamps = 420 – 150 = 270

   Amount more Singapore than U.S. stamps = 270 – 150 = 120

   Per cent more Singapore stamps than U.S stamps = $\frac{120}{150} \times 100\% = 80\%$

7. 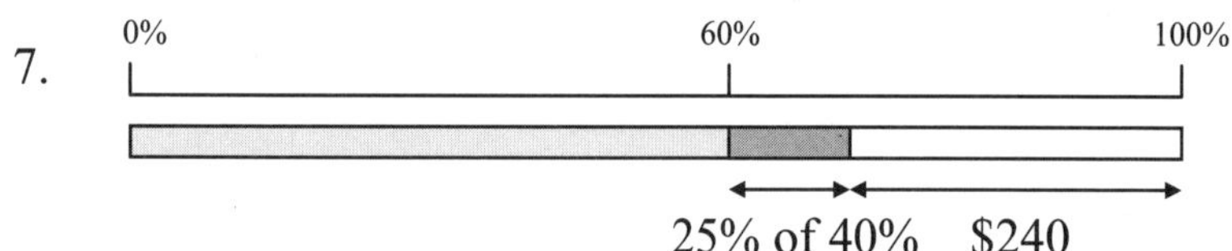

   Percentage left = 75% of 40% = $\frac{3}{4} \times 40\% = 30\%$

   $30\% \longrightarrow \$240$

   $1\% \longrightarrow \$\frac{240}{30}$

   $100\% \longrightarrow \$\frac{240}{30} \times 100 = \$800$

   The sum of money was $800.

8. Marvin's total stamps is 100%.

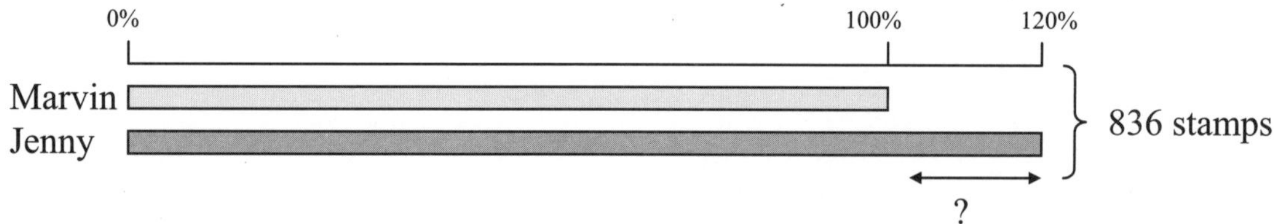

   Percentage both have = 220% of Marvin's stamps

   $220\% \longrightarrow 836$ stamps

   $1\% \longrightarrow \frac{836}{220}$

   $20\% \longrightarrow \frac{836}{220} \times 20 = 76$

   Jenny has 76 more stamps than Marvin.

9. 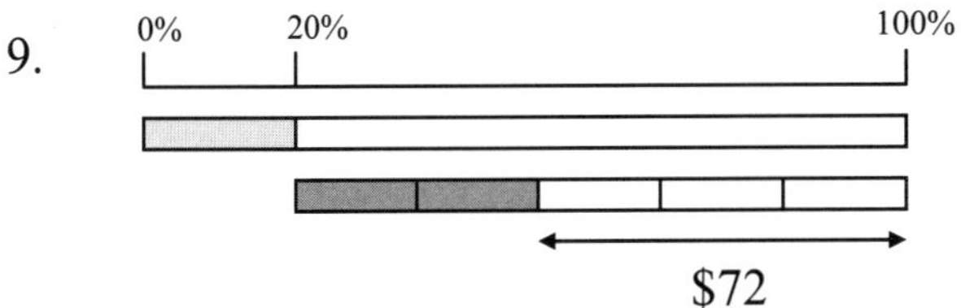

After buying the dress, the remainder is 80%.

Her money left after buying the book = $\frac{3}{5}$ of 80% = 48%

$48\% \longrightarrow \$72$

$1\% \longrightarrow \$\frac{72}{48}$

$100\% \longrightarrow \$\frac{72}{48} \times 100 = \$150$

She had $150 at first.

10. 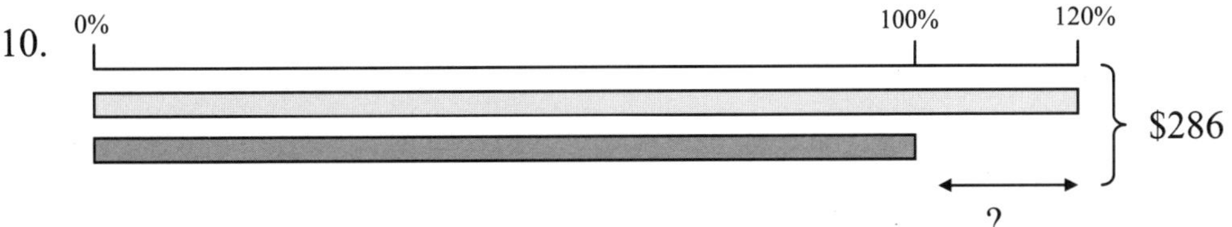

Total money received = 220% of cost price

$220\% \longrightarrow \$286$

$1\% \longrightarrow \$\frac{286}{220}$

$20\% \longrightarrow \$\frac{286}{220} \times 20 = \$26$

He earned $26.

Part 5: Speed — 2 sessions

Tasks 1-3, pp. 102-104 [3rd pp. 86-88]
Notes:

In these problems, we are dealing with 3 quantities, speed, time and distance. We can get the third quantity from the other two:
Distance = Speed × Time

$\text{Speed} = \dfrac{\text{Distance}}{\text{Time}}$

$\text{Time} = \dfrac{\text{Distance}}{\text{Speed}}$

Students can draw diagrams for these problems, using a line between two points to represent a trip or a part of it, and indicating all the given data. Usually the first step in solving these problems is to look at the part of the trip for which there are two pieces of data, and then use the formulas to find the unknown third piece of data.

To find the average speed for the whole distance, when a trip is divided into two parts, we need to first find the *total* distance and the *total* time of the whole trip.

#1. Lead students to see that to find the first driver's average speed, we need to find a time. We can get a time for the second driver (we have speed and distance for him), and use that to get the time for the first driver.

#2. We have two pieces of data for the first part: speed (75 km/h) and time (40 min). We can find the distance for the first part (speed × time). Since we have the total distance, we can now find the distance for the second part by subtraction. Now we have two pieces of data for the second part (speed and distance) and so can find the time for the second part.

#3. We have two pieces of data for the first part: speed (60 km/h) and time (2 h). We can find the distance for the first part. From this distance, we can determine the distance of the last part. Since we already have the speed for the last part, we can now find the time for the last part.

Practice 6G p. 105 [3rd 5G p. 89]

1. Distance = 70 km/h × 2 h = 140 km

   Time for return = $\dfrac{140\text{ km}}{80\text{ km/h}} = \dfrac{7}{4}\text{ h} = 1\dfrac{3}{4}\text{ h}$

   $1\dfrac{3}{4}$ h after 3:00 p.m. is 4:45 p.m.

   She reaches Town P at 4:45 p.m.

2 h, 70 km/h
P Q
80 km/h 3:00 p.m.

2. Time for van = $\frac{190 \text{ km}}{60 \text{ km/h}} = 3\frac{1}{6}$ h = 3 h 10 min.

If the car leaves 50 minutes after the van and arrives 20 minutes earlier, its travel time is 70 minutes less. 70 min = 1 h 10 min

Time for car = 3 h 10 min – 1 h 10 min = 2 h

Speed of car = $\frac{190 \text{ km}}{2 \text{ h}}$ = 95 km/h

3. Time for trip from P to Q = $\frac{120 \text{ km}}{40 \text{ km/h}}$ = 3 h

Time for return trip = $\frac{120 \text{ km}}{60 \text{ km/h}}$ = 2 h

Total time = 3 h + 2 h = 5 h

Total distance = 2 × 120 km = 240 km

Average speed = $\frac{240 \text{ km}}{5 \text{ h}}$ = 48 km/h

4.

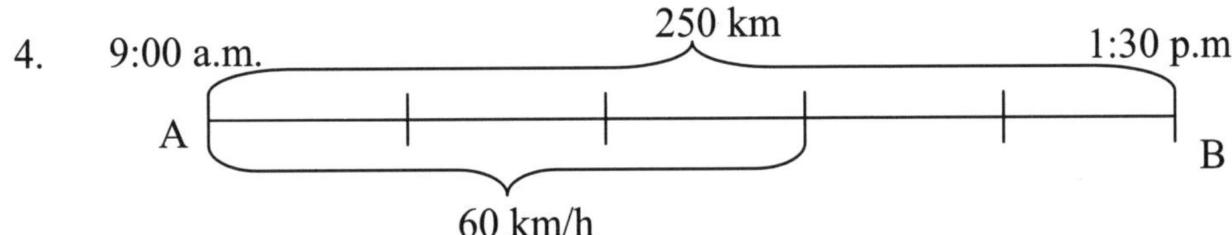

Distance for 1st part = $\frac{3}{5}$ × 250 km = 150 km

Distance for 2nd part = 250 km – 150 km = 100 km

Time for 1st part = $\frac{150 \text{ km}}{60 \text{ km/h}} = 2\frac{1}{2}$ h = 2 h 30 min

Total time = 4 h 30 min

Time for 2nd part = 4 h 30 min – 2 h 30 min = 2 h

Speed for 2nd part = $\frac{100 \text{ km}}{2 \text{ h}}$ = 50 km/h

5.

80 km/h

X Y

$\frac{1}{2}$ h, 70 km/h

Distance for 1st part = 70 km/h × $\frac{1}{2}$ h = 35 km

Distance for whole trip = 35 km × 4 = 140 km

Time for whole trip = $\frac{140 \text{ km}}{80 \text{ km/h}} = 1\frac{3}{4}$ h

Time for 2nd part = $1\frac{3}{4}$ h – $\frac{1}{2}$ h = $1\frac{1}{4}$ h

6.

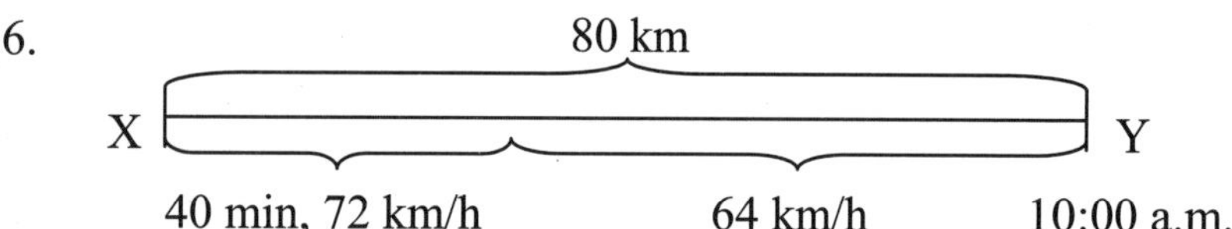

40 min = $\frac{40}{60}$ h = $\frac{2}{3}$ h

Distance for 1st part = 72 km/h × $\frac{2}{3}$ h = 48 km

Distance for 2nd part = 80 km – 48 km = 32 km

Time for 2nd part = $\frac{32 \text{ km}}{64 \text{ km/h}} = \frac{1}{2}$ h = 30 min

Total time = 40 min + 30 min = 70 min = 1 h 10 min
1 h 10 min before 10:00 a.m. is 8:50 a.m.
He left Town X at 8:50 a.m.

7.

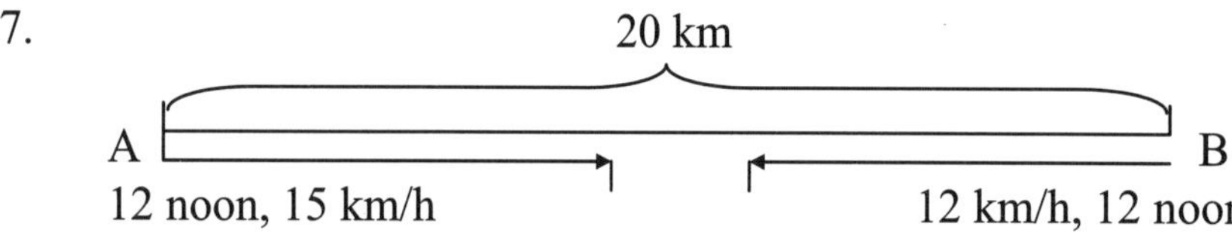

Time for both = $\frac{2}{3}$ h

Distance for Peter = 15 km/h × $\frac{2}{3}$ h = 10 km

Distance for Henry = 12 km/h × $\frac{2}{3}$ h = 8 km

Distance still between them = 20 – 10 – 8 = 2 km

Review

Objectives

- Review previous material.

Suggested number of sessions: 4

	Objectives	Textbook
67-70	▪ Review	Review F Review G USReview H

Possible solutions for selected problems are given here. These solutions emphasize use of bar models or a unitary approach where appropriate. Other solutions are possible.

Starred problems in the text are more challenging.

Review F pp. 106-110 [3rd pp. 90-194]

17. The sum of the two numbers is $56 \times 2 = 112$
1 unit = the larger number
2 units = $112 + 10 = 122$
1 unit = $122 \div 2 = 61$
The larger number is 61.

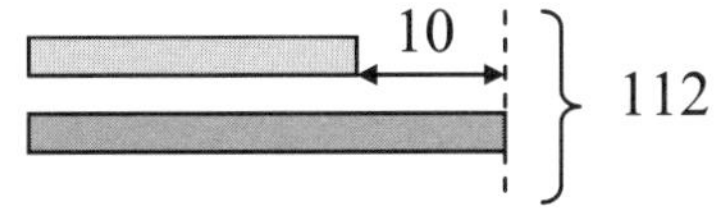

18. Mary Alice US: Cody 3rd: Devi

Fraction Cody [Devi] received
$= \frac{5}{9} \times \frac{3}{4} = \frac{5}{12}$

19. Total weight = 34 kg × 2 = 68 kg
8 units = 68 kg
1 unit = $68 \div 8 = 8.5$ kg
5 units = $8.5 \times 5 = 42.5$ kg
Kyle [Raju] weighs 42.5 kg

US: Kyle, Colin — 3rd: Raju, Gopal

20.

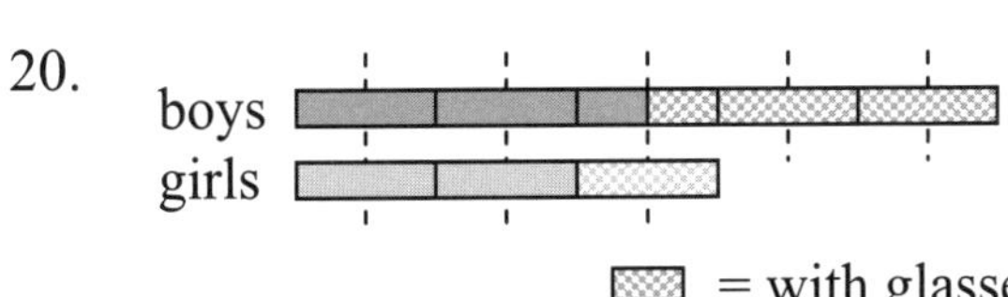

Fraction of the children with glasses = $\frac{7}{16}$

Or: Fraction of the children with glasses = $\left(\frac{1}{3} \times \frac{3}{8}\right) + \left(\frac{1}{2} \times \frac{5}{8}\right) = \frac{1}{8} + \frac{5}{16} = \frac{2}{16} + \frac{5}{16} = \frac{7}{16}$

23.

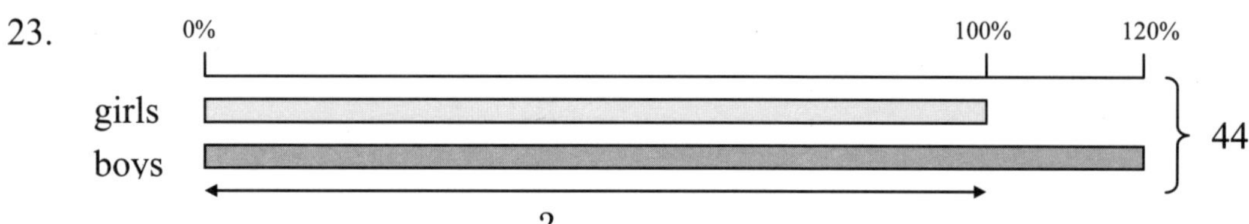

Number of girls is 100%.
Total number of students is 220% of the number of girls.

$220\% \longrightarrow 44$

$1\% \longrightarrow \frac{44}{220}$

$100\% \longrightarrow \frac{44}{220} \times 100 = 20$

There are 20 girls.

25. 1 unit = cost of skirt with shirt together = $30
Total number of skirt with shirt units = $80 – $20 = $60
Number of $30 skirt with shirt units = $60 ÷ $30 = 2
She bought 2 units of skirt with shirt plus 2 more shirts.
She bought a total of 4 shirts.

29.

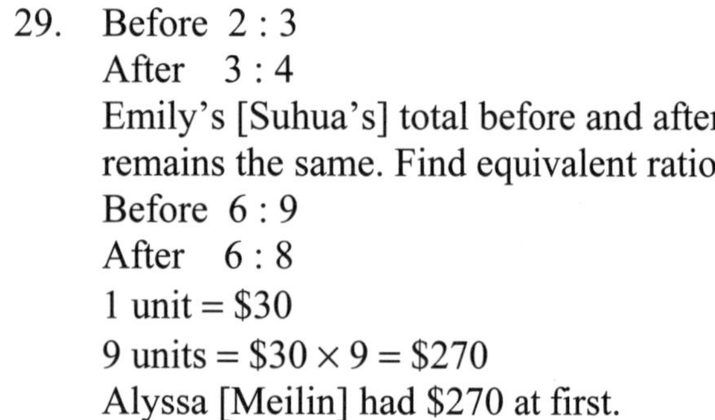

Before 2 : 3
After 3 : 4
Emily's [Suhua's] total before and after remains the same. Find equivalent ratio.
Before 6 : 9
After 6 : 8
1 unit = $30
9 units = $30 × 9 = $270
Alyssa [Meilin] had $270 at first.

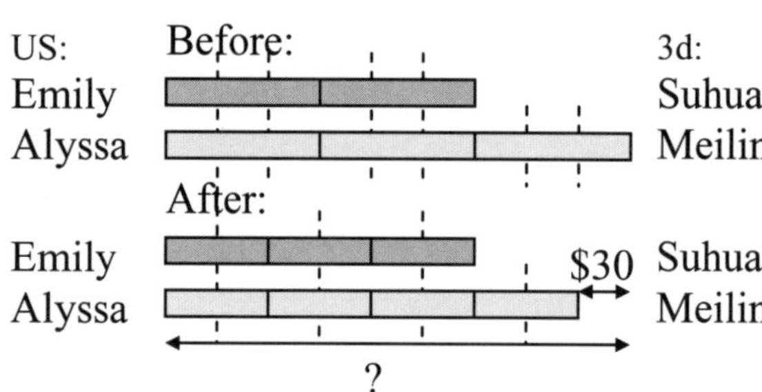

30.

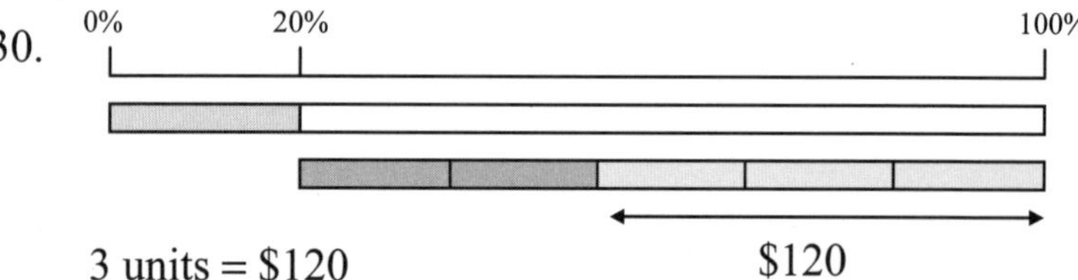

3 units = $120
1 unit = $120 ÷ 3 = $40
5 units = $40 × 5 = $200
5 units, or 80% of the money, was divided between Susan and Lauren [3rd: Sufen and Liling]
80% → $200
10% → $200 ÷ 8 = $25
20% → $25 × 2 = $50
Kristi [Meihua] received $50

32.

? km

P Q

12:00, 15 km/h 12:30 12:10, 12 km/h

The distance between the two towns is the sum of the distances traveled by Henry and Paul.

Time for Henry = 12:00 noon to 12:30 p.m. = $\frac{1}{2}$ h

Distance for Henry = 15 km/h × $\frac{1}{2}$ h = $7\frac{1}{2}$ km = 7.5 km

Time for Paul = 12:10 p.m. to 12:30 p.m. = 20 min = $\frac{20}{60}$ h = $\frac{1}{3}$ h

Distance for Paul = 12 km/h × $\frac{1}{3}$ h = 4 km

Distance between the towns = 7.5 km + 4 km = 11.5 km

Review G, pp. 111-116 [3rd pp. 95-100]

23. 1 orange costs \$$\frac{1}{5}$ = \$0.20, and 1 apple costs \$$\frac{1}{4}$ = \$0.25. He bought an equal number of each. He paid \$0.05 or 5¢ more for an apple than for an orange. To have spent \$1.00, or 100¢ more on apples than on oranges, he would have bought $\frac{100}{5}$ = 20 pairs of apples and oranges. So he bought 20 apples.

24.

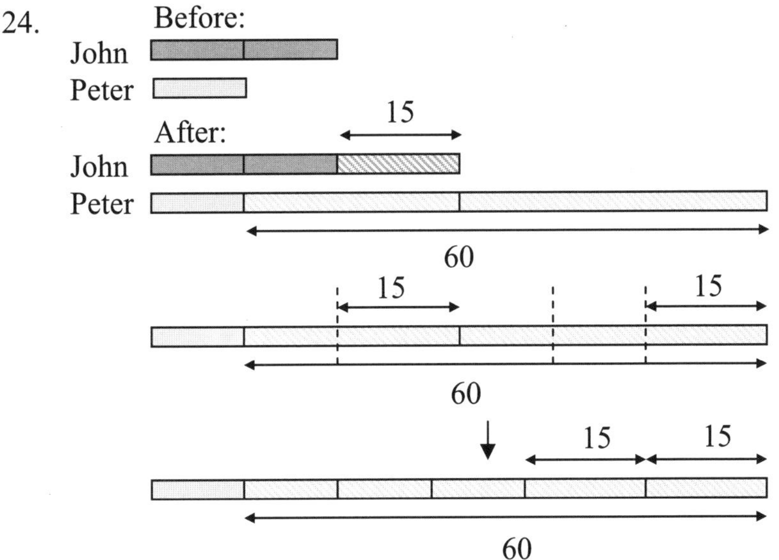

1 unit = Peter's stamps, before

Half of Peter's bar, after, is equal to John's bar, so each half of Peter's bar is equal to 2 units + 15. So 3 units + 2 parts of 15 = 60 stamps. You can rearrange the units to show this.

3 units = 60 – (2 × 15)
= 60 – 30 = 30

1 unit = 30 ÷ 3 = 10

Peter had 10 stamps at first.

27. US: After: 3rd:

Nicky Gopal

Kyle $120 Raju

Before: $20

Nicky Gopal

Kyle $20 Raju

8 units = $120

3 units = $\$\frac{120}{8} \times 3 = \$45$

Amount Nicky originally had = $45 + $20 = $65

28.

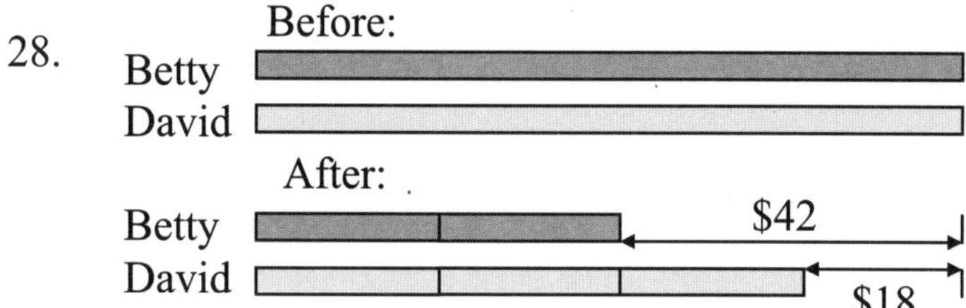

1 unit = $42 – $18 = $24

2 units = $24 × 2 = $48

Amount Betty had = $48 + $42 = $90

Each of them had $90.

29.

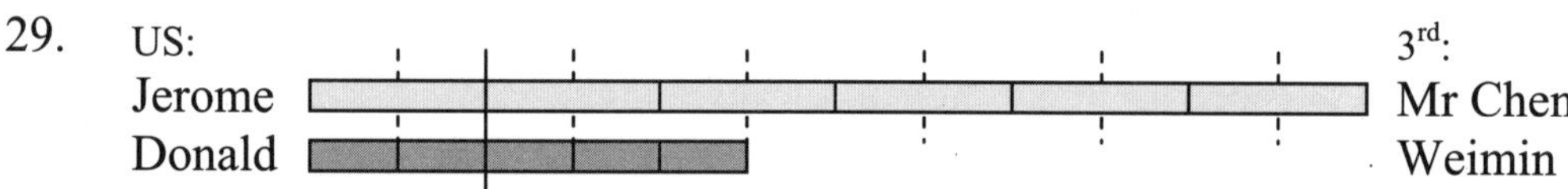

Ratio = **12 : 5**

OR:

$\frac{1}{6}$ of Jerome's weight = $\frac{2}{5}$ of Donald's weight

All of Jerome's weight = $\frac{2}{5} \times 6 = \frac{12}{5}$ of Donald's weight.

Jerome's weight : Donald's weight = **12 : 5**

30. Before 3 : 2

After 6 : 1

Justin's (Mingli's) money stays the same. Find equivalent ratios where the number of Justin's (Mingli's) units is the same.

Before 6 : 4

After 6 : 1

3 units = $15

1 unit = $15 ÷ 3 = $5

4 units = $5 × 4 = $20

Scott (Suhua) had $20.

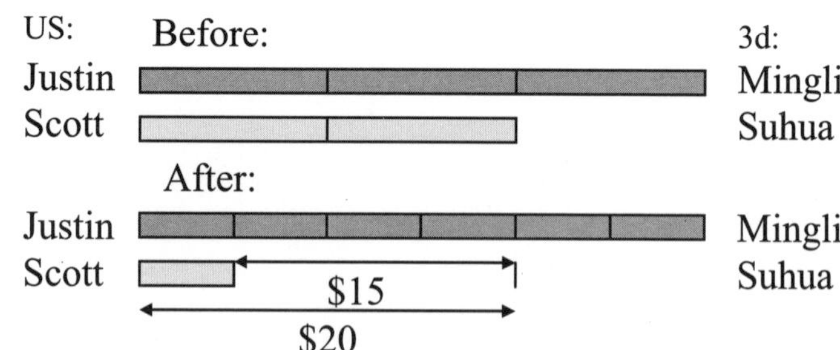

31. Peter and Marry began with the same amount of money. The final ratio of Peter's money to Mary's money is 5 : 4, so Mary ends up with 4 units. If she spent $\frac{1}{3}$ of her money, she had had 6 units originally and spent 2 of them in order to end up with 4 units.. Peter must also have started with 6 units. He spent 1 unit to end up with 5 units..
1 unit = \$50
5 units = \$50 × 5 = \$250
Peter had \$250 left.

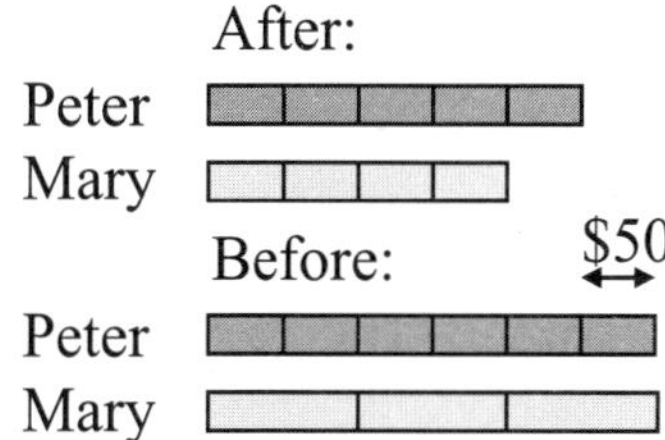

32. 0% 80% 100%

\$2400 left in bank

The money he took out of the bank is 100%. So the money in the bank is 200% of his withdrawal. 80% of his withdrawal is \$2400.

$80\% \rightarrow \$2400$

$10\% \rightarrow \$\frac{2400}{8} = \$300$

$200\% \rightarrow \$\frac{2400}{8} \times 20 = \$6000$

He had \$6000 in the bank.

34. The distance traveled in both cases is the same.
Distance = 45 km/h × 2 h = 90 km
Speed for case 2 = 45 km/h + 5 km/h = 50 km/h

Time for case 2 = $\frac{90 \text{ km}}{50 \text{ km/h}} = 1\frac{4}{5}$ h

$\frac{4}{5} \times 60$ min = 4 × 12 min = 48 min

He would take 1 h 48 min.

36. (3rd: Chris is Ahmad and Chad is Daud)

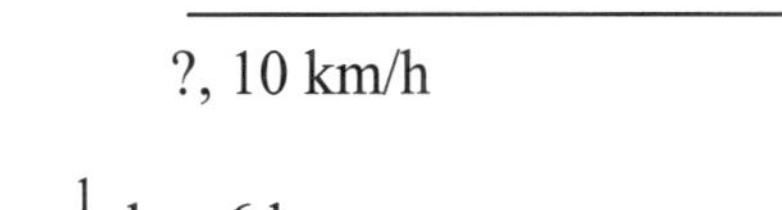

Time for Chris = $\frac{1}{2}$ h

Distance between the towns

= Chris's speed × Chris's time = 12 km/h × $\frac{1}{2}$ h = 6 km

Distance for Chad = 6 km − 1.5 km = 4.5 km

Time for Chad = $\frac{4.5 \text{ km}}{10 \text{ km/h}}$ = 0.45 h = 0.45 × 60 min = 27 min

27 min before 8:30 a.m. is 8:03 a.m.
Chad left Town A at 8:03 a.m.

38. Distance for John = 6 km/h × 3 h = 18 km
Distance for Peter = 27 km – 18 km = 9 km
Speed for Peter = $\frac{9\text{ km}}{3\text{ h}}$ = 3 km/h

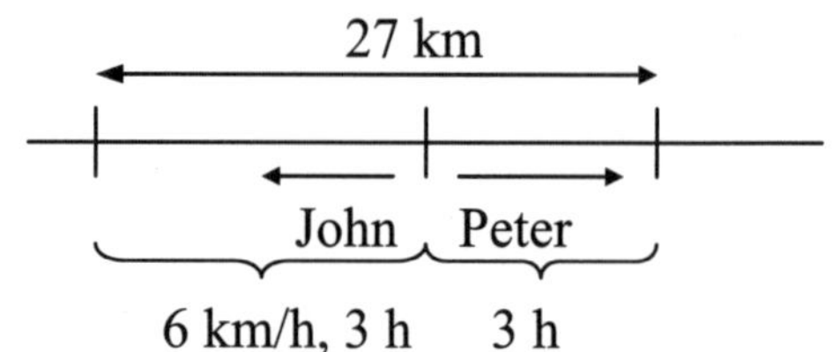

41. The area of the shaded part is the area of both squares minus the area of the two larger unshaded triangles, one of which traverses both squares.
Shaded area = $(6 \times 6) + (4 \times 4) - (\frac{1}{2} \times 10 \times 4) - (\frac{1}{2} \times 6 \times 6)$
$= 36 + 16 - 20 - 18 = 14$ in.^{2} [3rd cm^2]

US edition only: Review H pp. 117-120

6. Area of rectangle = 16×7
Both triangles have the same height, so bases can be added to find total area of both triangles.
Area of triangles = $\frac{1}{2} \times 8 \times 7 = 4 \times 7$
Fraction shaded = $\frac{4 \times 7}{16 \times 7} = \frac{1}{4}$
(Note: Calculations are saved until the end, making the computation easier. Point out to students that calculations do not need to be done at each step.)

13. 2 × \$3.60 = \$7.20
12 oz = $\frac{3}{4}$ lb; $\frac{3}{4}$ × \$3.60 = \$2.70
\$7.20 + \$2.70 = \$9.90

14. Weight of cooking oil = 2.5 lb – 11 oz = (2.5 × 16 oz) – 11 oz = 40 oz – 11 oz = 29 oz

16. If 1 pt of water poured from A to B results in the same amount of water in both, A must have 2 more pints than B.

4 units = 5 + 2 + 5 = 12 pt
1 unit = 12 pt ÷ 4 = 3 pt.
Total water = 6 units
6 units = 3 pt × 6 = 18 pt

25.

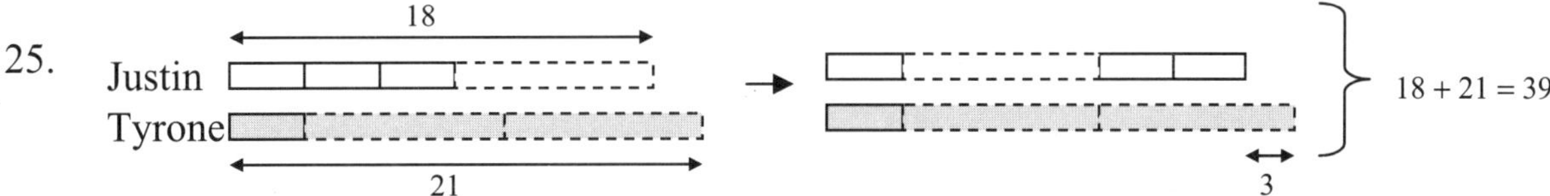

One long unit (unit given away) is 3 more than 2 short units.
Make each long unit into 2 short units + 3

10 units = 39 – (3 × 3) = 30
1 unit = 3
Justin gave away 18 – (3 × 3) = 18 – 9 = 9

OR
Make a list of how many marbles each boy has each time Justin gives away 1 and Tyrone gives away 2 until the ratio of their number of marbles is 3 : 1.

Justin	Tyrone
18	21
17	19
16	17
15	15
14	13
13	11
12	9
11	7
10	5
9	3

So Justin gave away 9 marbles.

27. The ratio of their speeds is $\frac{65}{55} = \frac{13}{11}$

So the car travels 13 units at the same time the truck travels 11 units.
They both travel a total of 24 units. Divide the distance into 24 units.
360 ÷ 24 = 15
Each unit is 15 mi.
Distance car travels in the same length of time = 13 × 15 mi = 195 mi
Distance truck travels in the same length of time = 11 × 15 = 165 mi
Time for car = Distance ÷ Speed = 195 mi ÷ 65 mi/h = 3 h
They pass after 3 h.
3 h after 10:30 a.m. is 1:30 p.m.
OR:
Consider both vehicles as a single one that goes 360 miles at 65 mi/h + 55 mi/h = 120 mi/h.
This takes = $\frac{360}{120}$ = 3 h, so the vehicles would pass each other at 1:30 p.m.
OR:
The cars are approaching each other, closing the gap at a rate of 65 mi/h + 55 mi/h = 120 mi/h.
Together they have to go 360 miles, so they will pass each other after $\frac{360}{120}$ = 3 h, or at 1:30 p.m.

28. Time to destination = 150 mi ÷ 50 mi/h = 3 h
Time spent so far = 3 h 30 min, time is now 3:30 p.m.
Time for return to get back by 6:00 p.m. is $2\frac{1}{2}$ h.
Speed at which he must travel = 150 mi ÷ $2\frac{1}{2}$ h = $150 \div \frac{5}{2} = 150 \times \frac{2}{5}$ = 60 mi/h

29. 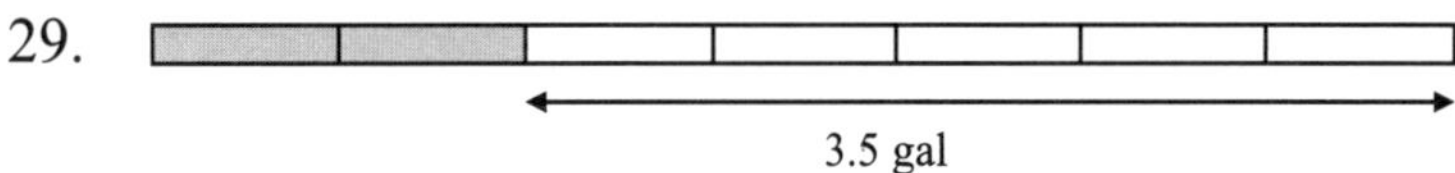

5 units = 3.5 gal
1 unit = 3.5 ÷ 5 = 0.7 gal
If 2.1 gal were added, 3 units would be added, and 5 out of 7 units would be filled.
The fraction of the tank filled would be $\frac{5}{7}$.

Textbook Answer Key

US: Unit 1 – Fractions

US: Part 1: Division (pp. 6-9)

1. 6
2. (a) 4; 4 (b) 5; 10
3. (a) 8 (b) 36 (c) 21
   (d) 32 (e) 15 (f) 81
4. $\frac{1}{8}$
5. (a) $\frac{1}{2}$; $\frac{1}{6}$ (b) $\frac{1}{8}$; $\frac{1}{10}$
6. (a) $\frac{1}{6}$ (b) $\frac{1}{24}$ (c) $\frac{1}{30}$
   (d) $\frac{2}{9}$ (e) $\frac{1}{7}$ (f) $\frac{1}{18}$
7. 2
8. (a) 3; 2 (b) 6; 4
9. (a) $\frac{1}{2}$ (b) 4 (c) 6
   (d) 5 (e) $\frac{2}{3}$ (f) $\frac{3}{2}$
10. 4
11. (a) $\frac{8}{3}$; $\frac{8}{3}$ (b) $\frac{5}{4}$; $\frac{5}{2}$
    (c) $\frac{9}{2}$; $\frac{3}{2}$ (d) $\frac{3}{2}$; $\frac{5}{4}$
12. (a) $\frac{9}{2}$ (b) 10 (c) $\frac{14}{3}$
    (d) $\frac{10}{9}$ (e) $\frac{2}{3}$ (f) $\frac{25}{16}$

US: Practice 1A (p. 10)

1. (a) 6 (b) 20 (c) 9
2. (a) $\frac{1}{10}$ (b) $\frac{1}{12}$ (c) $\frac{1}{14}$
3. (a) $\frac{1}{2}$ (b) $\frac{8}{3}$ (c) $\frac{9}{2}$
4. (a) $\frac{1}{4}$ (b) $\frac{5}{6}$ (c) $\frac{32}{25}$
5. (a) 18 (b) 4
6. 8
7. 12
8. 15
9. 9
10. $\frac{2}{5}$
11. $\frac{1}{5}$ m

US: Part 2: Order of Operations (pp. 11-14)

3; $3\frac{1}{4}$

1. 7
2. (a) $\frac{19}{12}$ (b) $\frac{5}{12}$ (c) $\frac{3}{20}$
   (d) $\frac{2}{9}$ (e) $\frac{2}{5}$ (f) $\frac{7}{8}$
3. $\frac{35}{24}$
4. $\frac{3}{5}$
5. 1
6. $\frac{5}{12}$
7. (a) $\frac{5}{4}$ (b) 2
   (c) $\frac{5}{27}$ (d) $\frac{1}{4}$
   (e) 2 (f) $\frac{8}{9}$
8. $\frac{15}{4}$; $7\frac{3}{4}$
9. $\frac{2}{15}$; $\frac{13}{15}$
10. (a) $2\frac{11}{12}$ (b) $11\frac{1}{2}$
    (c) 18 (d) 23
    (e) $\frac{7}{6}$ (f) $4\frac{2}{5}$
11. $\frac{1}{4}$; $\frac{1}{8}$
12. $\frac{1}{12}$; $\frac{11}{12}$
13. (a) $\frac{17}{20}$ (b) $\frac{13}{30}$
    (c) $2\frac{1}{8}$ (d) $\frac{1}{9}$

(e) $\frac{13}{18}$ (f) $\frac{3}{8}$

14. $\frac{3}{10}$; $\frac{3}{40}$

15. (a) $\frac{7}{3}$ (b) 3

(c) $\frac{1}{2}$ (d) $\frac{1}{3}$

(e) $\frac{1}{8}$ (f) $\frac{68}{45}$

US: Practice 1B (p. 15)

1. (a) $\frac{5}{12}$ (b) $\frac{9}{8}$
   (c) $\frac{4}{3}$ (d) $\frac{1}{12}$
   (e) 1 (f) 2
2. (a) 9 (b) 2
   (c) 24 (d) $2\frac{1}{12}$
   (e) $3\frac{1}{3}$ (f) $5\frac{1}{2}$
3. (a) $\frac{3}{2}$ (b) $\frac{1}{12}$
   (c) $\frac{3}{20}$ (d) $\frac{3}{4}$
   (e) $\frac{1}{6}$ (f) $\frac{1}{2}$
4. (a) 3 (b) 20
   (c) 1 (d) $\frac{5}{2}$
   (e) $\frac{1}{20}$ (f) 12
5. (a) 6 (b) 16
   (c) $6\frac{3}{10}$ (d) $\frac{19}{30}$
   (e) $\frac{7}{8}$ (f) $\frac{1}{15}$

US: Part 3: Word Problems (pp. 16-19)

300; 1000

1. (b) 84
2. (b) $300
3. $24
4. 120
5. 200
6. 40

US: Practice 1C (p. 20)

1. 25
2. 30
3. 50
4. 360
5. $75
6. $8
7. $480
8. 120
9. 12 lb

US: Practice 1D (p. 21)

1. $2400
2. $360
4. $36
5. 300
6. $6
7. $20
8. 20

US: Unit 2 – Circles
3rd: Unit 1 – Circles

Part 1: Radius and Diameter (US pp. 22-25 3rd pp. 6-9)

1. (a) 3 cm (b) 4 cm (c) 6 cm
2. radius = 5 cm, diameter = 10 cm
6. (a) 8 cm (b) 9 cm
7. (a) B (b) D
   (c) 16 m, 10 m, 8 cm, 14 cm

Part 2: Circumference (US: pp. 26-29 3rd pp. 10-13)

2. 188.4 cm
3. 157 cm
4. 88 cm
5. 220 cm
6. 25.12 m
7. (a) 154 cm (b) 88 cm (c) 44 m
8. (a) 31.4 m (b) 18.84 cm
   (c) 37.68 m

9. 10.28 m
10. 15π cm
11. 104 cm

US: Practice 2A (p. 30)
3rd: Practice 1A (p. 14)

1. 62.8 cm
2. 220 cm
3. 72.2 cm
4. 25.12 cm
5. 88 cm
6. 20π cm

Part 3: Area (US pp. 31-35, 3rd pp. 15-19)

1. 314 cm^2
2. 616 cm^2
3. 50.24 cm^2
4. 154 m^2
5. 113.04 m^2
6. (a) 616 cm^2 (b) 1386 cm^2
   (c) 616 m^2
7. (a) 28.26 cm^2 (b) 78.5 cm^2
   (d) 200.96 m^2
8. (a) 56.52 cm^2 (b) 157 cm^2
9. (a) 3.14 m^2 (b) 78.5 cm^2
10. (a) 113.04 cm^2 (b) 28.26 m^2
11. (a) 1257 m^2
12. (a) $1\frac{1}{2}\pi$ cm^2

US: Practice 2B (p. 36)
3rd: Practice 1B (p. 20)

1. 113.04 cm^2
2. 616 m^2
3. (a) 12.56 cm (b) 12.56 cm^2
4. 1.57 m^2
5. US: 78.5 in^2 3rd: 78 cm^2
6. 28.26 cm^2; 18.84 cm
7. 154 cm^2

US: Practice 2C (p. 37)
3rd: Practice 1C (p. 21)

1. (a) 504 cm^2 (b) 88 cm
2. 63.25 m^2; 29.7 m
3. 38.88 cm^2; 36.56 cm
4. 2π m^2; 3π m
5. 12π cm^2

US: Unit 3 – Graphs
3rd: Unit 3 – Graphs

Part 1: Pie Charts (US pp. 38-41, 3rd pp. 22-25)

1. (a) plastic (b) 50
   (c) $\frac{2}{5}$ (d) 2
2. (a) $\frac{1}{4}$ (b) \$12,000
   (c) \$1200 (d) 8 : 5
3. (a) US: toast 3rd: bread
   (b) $\frac{1}{20}$ (c) 24
   (d) 25%
4. (a) $\frac{1}{2}$ (b) 25%
   (c) $\frac{1}{8}$ (d) 600
5. (a) swimming (b) 15%
   (c) 60% (d) $\frac{7}{20}$
6. (a) US: shirts 3rd: blouses
   (b) 35%
   (c) 30% (d) \$200

Review A (US pp. 42-47, 3rd pp. 26-31)

1. Two million, three hundred forty thousand
2. 0.57
3. 2
4. 7
5. 0.09, 0.123, 0.25, 0.5
6. 5.59 kg
7. $\frac{1}{8}$
8. $\frac{3}{8}$
9. 2
10. US: $\frac{7}{20}$ 3rd: 21.49
11. 600.93
12. 41.86

13. 17
14. 35,000
15. 67.5
16. (a) 80 min (b) 20 g
17. 8
18. $200
19. 26
20. 0.32 kg
21. 38 kg
22. 36 kg
23. $\frac{7}{20}$
24. $\frac{4}{9}$
25. $20
26. 360
27. 4
28. 25%
29. 25%
30. $28
31. 120 km
32. $240
33. $7.15
34. $860
35. $960
36. 3 : 4
37. $2000
38. $120
39. 12.5 km/h
40. (a) $2\frac{1}{3}$ (b) 36
41. $\frac{3x-2}{2}$ kg
42. 81 cm^2
43. 45.7 cm
44. D
45. 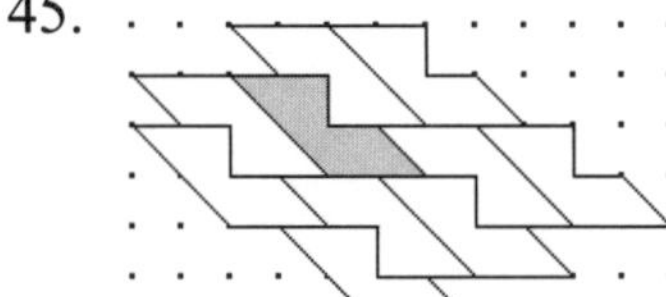
46. (a) Thursday (b) 5% (c) 37
47. (a) 18% (b) $\frac{1}{5}$ (c) 150

Review B (US pp. 48-53, 3rd pp. 32-37)

1. 4
2. 1000
3. (a) 10,000 (b) 0.06
4. 36
5. 2.53
6. 9.009
7. $\frac{1}{3}$
8. 1000
9. (a) $\frac{6}{125}$ (b) $\frac{9}{25}$
10. $\frac{12}{25}, \frac{3}{5}, \frac{62}{100}, \frac{31}{20}$
11. (a) 4 (b) US: $5\frac{3}{10}$ 3rd: 40
12. 100
13. 11 h 15 min
14. 16
15. 850 g
16. 60
17. 8
18. 16
19. 41
20. 25 min
21. $\frac{1}{6}$
22. $\frac{5}{8}$
23. (a) 12 (b) 7
24. US: 35 yd 3rd: 35 m
25. 12%
26. 75%
27. $4.50
28. 1.25 m/s
29. 10
30. $10
31. 16
32. 24
33. US: 50 lb 3rd: 50 kg
34. $240
35. 18%
36. 25%
37. 85 km/h
38. US: 48 $in.^2$ 3rd: cm^2
39. 57.5 cm^2

40. 31.4 cm
41. Two lines of symmetry:

42. 9
43. C
44. (a) 40 (b) 25%
(c) 8 (d) 80
45. (a) $1800 (b) $1880 (c) 600

US: Unit 4 – Volume
3rd: Unit 3 – Volume

Part 1: Solving Problems (US pp. 54-58, 3rd pp. 54-58)

125
1. 80 cm^3
2. 75
3. 15 cm
4. 4.4 ℓ
5. 36 cm; 54 cm
6. 1750 cm^3
7. 1.5 cm; 21.5 cm
8. 20 min
9. 0.65 min

US: Practice 4A (p. 59)
3rd: Practice 3A (p. 43)

1. 36 cm^2
2. 8 cm
3. (a) 4 (b) 8
4. (a) 27 cm^3 (b) 324 cm^3
5. (a) 32 cm^3 (b) 72 cm^2

US: Practice 4B (p. 60)
3rd: Practice 3B (p. 44)

1. 4.5 cm
2. 10.8 cm
3. (a) 168 ℓ (b) 21 min
4. 40 cm

US: Practice 4C (p. 61)
3rd: Practice 2C (p. 45)

1. 11.6 cm
2. (a) 105,000 cm^3
(b) 8750 cm^3
3. 6.5 min
4. 6000 cm^3

US: Unit 5 - Triangles and 4-Sided Figures
3rd: Unit 4 - Triangles and 4-Sided Figures

Part 1: Finding Unknown Angles (US pp. 62-65, 3rd pp. 46-49)

angle p = 60°, angle q = 120°,
angle r = 120°, angle s = 60°
1. 71, 109
2. 98, 132
3. 84, 48
4. 52, 128, 128
5. 45, 135, 22.5
6. 62, 152, 14
7. 65, 80, 15

US: Practice 5A (p. 66)
3rd: Practice 4A (p. 50)

1. $\angle a = 50° \angle b = 58°$
2. $\angle p = 38° \angle q = 104°$
3. $\angle x = 80°$
4. $\angle m = 82°$
5. $\angle h = 66°$

US: Practice 5B (p. 67)
3rd: Practice 4B (p. 51)

1. $\angle p = 60° \angle q = 124°$
2. $\angle a = 34° \angle b = 56°$
3. $\angle x = 125°$ $\angle y = 27.5°$
4. $\angle m = 24°$
5. $\angle w = 40°$

Review C (US pp. 68-72, 3rd pp. 52-56)

1. (a) 30,030 (b) 3,040,000
2. (a) 100 (b) 0.09
3. 3400

4. 6
5. $33\frac{1}{3}$
6. $690
7. $\frac{2}{9}$
8. 54 ℓ
9. US: (a) $1\frac{1}{4}$ (b) $10\frac{1}{3}$
   3rd: 9. 8 : 2 : 5
10. 6 : 1
11. $\frac{5}{3}$
12. 40%
13. 15%
14. 40%
15. $\frac{1}{40}$
16. $2.90
17. 4 km/h
18. $75
19. 135 ℓ
20. (a) 1 : 2 (b) 20
21. 96 cm^2
22. 54 km/h
23. 80 km/h
24. 4t – 2
25. $(40 – 3*n*)
26. 60°
27. 22.5°
28. 80°
29. 60.5 cm^2
30. 6π m^2
31. 8 cm
32. 1.8 min
33. (a) US: 2.2 gal 3rd: 2.2 ℓ
    (b) C (c) $\frac{3}{5}$

Review D (US pp. 73-77, 3rd pp. 57-61)

1. (a) 600 (b) 1000
2. (a) 8 (b) 50
3. 13.28
4. (a) 0.375 (b) 0.82
5. $\frac{3}{15}$
6. 1.4
7. 9:25 a.m.
8. (a) $\frac{2}{25}$ (b) $4\frac{7}{25}$
9. (a) 32% (b) 45%
10. $\frac{11}{80}$
11. US: $\frac{4}{3}$ 3rd: 36%
12. (a) 5 (b) 6 : 9 : 15
13. $5
14. $244
15. $\frac{11}{18}$
16. $\frac{1}{3}$
17. $4.50
18. $340
19. (a) $38.50 (b) $60
20. 5 min
21. 181
22. 140
23. $150
24. 7 : 4 : 3
25. 140
26. 2 : 1 : 3
27. $120
28. 21%
29. 10:24 a.m.
30. 4 km/h
31. 11a + 3
32. 307 cm^2
33. 3 cm
34. 106°
35. C
36. 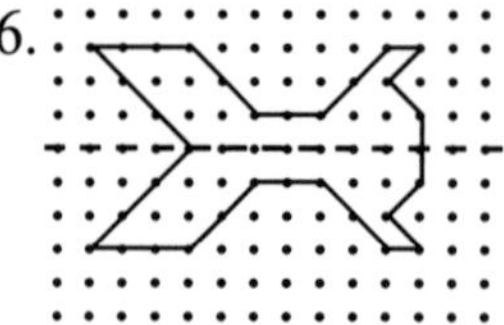
37. (a) 50 ℓ (b) 150 ℓ (c) $230

Review E (US pp. 78-82, 3rd pp. 62-66)

1. 0.8
2. 26,000
3. 40
4. 430 g
5. $\frac{3}{5}$
6. $\frac{4}{5}$
7. 0.08
8. $2\frac{2}{25}$
9. 2 m, $2\frac{1}{4}$ m, 2.49 m, 2.6 m
10. $\frac{3}{8}$
11. 8
12. $30
13. $6.50
14. 2025
15. 9
16. 12
17. 6
18. 3 : 2
19. 48 kg
20. $48
21. 6.25%
22. 12
23. 1,500
24. 60 km
25. 40
26. $0.90
27. $3.50
28. $270
29. $225
30. 1.2 kg
31. 5 : 8
32. 50
33. 5x + 36
34. 24 cm
35. 75 cm^2
36. 41.4 cm
37. 192 cm^2
38. 40 cm
39. 37°
40. 85°
41. 9
42. (a) $\frac{1}{4}$ (b) $\frac{1}{8}$ (c) 960

US: Unit 6 – More Challenging Word Problems
3rd: Unit 5 – More Challenging Word Problems

US: Practice 6A (p. 87)
3rd: Practice 5A (p. 71)

1. 132
2. $20
3. $22
4. $7.15
5. $21
6. 12
7. $15
8. 195
9. $480
10. 28

US: Practice 6B (p. 92)
3rd: Practice 5B (p. 76)

1. $36
2. $20
3. 20
4. $480
5. 12
6. $300
7. $30
8. 5

US: Practice 6C (p. 93)
3rd: Practice 5C (p. 77)

1. 225
2. $56
3. $225
4. 90
5. US: 0.9 lb 3rd: 0.9 kg
6. $168
7. $12
8. $100

US: Practice 6D (p. 97)
3rd: Practice 5D (p. 81)

1. 5 : 6
2. 48
3. 60
4. 1176 g
5. 15 cm
6. $37.50
7. 2 : 1
8. 5 : 12
9. 9 : 5
10. 4 : 5

US: Practice 6E (p. 98)
3rd: Practice 5E (p. 82)

1. 6 : 1
2. 8 : 5
3. $48
4. 120
5. $140
6. 600 ml
7. 28
8. $140
9. $32

US: Practice 6F (p. 101)
3rd: Practice 5F (p. 85)

1. 500
2. 68%
3. 82
4. 50%
5. 60%
6. 80%
7. $800
8. 76
9. $150
10. $26

US: Practice 6G (p. 105)
3rd: Practice 5G (p. 89)

1. 4:45 p.m.
2. 95 km/h
3. 48 km/h
4. 50 km/h
5. $1\frac{1}{4}$ h
6. 8:50 a.m.
7. 2 km

Review F (US pp. 106-110, 3rd pp. 90-94)

1. (a) 356,000 (b) 4.3
2. 0.103
3. $\frac{3}{8}$
4. $\frac{9}{200}$
5. 24
6. US: $\frac{13}{24}$ 3rd: $4\frac{1}{6}$
7. (a) 16 (b) $\frac{19}{20}$
8. (a) 1000 (b) 1000
9. 75¢
10. 96.5%
11. (a) 4 : 5 (b) 80%
12. (a) $\frac{3}{8}$ (b) $\frac{5}{3}$
13. $52.50
14. $800
15. 6 h
16. $16
17. 61
18. $\frac{5}{12}$
19. 42.5 kg
20. $\frac{7}{16}$
21. 60%
22. 40%
23. 20
24. 54 km
25. 4
26. $25
27. $120
28. 3 : 4
29. $270
30. $50
31. $1\frac{1}{2}$ h
32. 11.5 km

33. 3
34. \$2m
35. 70°
36. 120°
37. 105°
38. 10 cm^2
39. 25.7 cm
40. 8 cm
41. 10 cm
42. (a) 36 (b) 30% (c) 10.5

Review G (US pp. 111-116, 3rd pp. 95-100)

1. (a) 10,027 (b) 2,012,000
2. 20
3. 107,802
4. 30%
5. 450 g
6. 2.17
7. $\frac{2}{5}$
8. (a) 12 (b) 3
9. 7:45 a.m.
10. (a) 1 h 15 min (b) 2 km 300 m
11. (a) 800 m (b) 600 ml
    (c) 1350 g (d) 4 m 80 cm
12. US: 20 3rd: 25
13. 15
14. \$7.60
15. 33
16. \$3.40
17. \$32
18. (a) $\frac{1}{3}$ (b) \$450
19. \$336
20 \$12
21. \$32
22. 5 km
23. 20
24. 10
25. $\frac{3}{8}$
26. $\frac{4}{9}$
27. \$65
28. \$90
29. 12 : 5
30. \$20
31. \$250
32. \$6000
33. (a) 25 (b) 12
34. $1\frac{4}{5}$ h or 1 h 48 min
35. 58 km/h
36. 8.03 a.m.
37. 10:24 a.m.
38. 3 km/h
39. 41.4 cm
40. 42 cm^2
41. US: 14 $in.^2$ 3rd: 14 cm^2
42. 203 cm^2
43. 27 cm
44. 18°
45. 55°
46. (a) 22 (b) 8 (c) 17

US: Review H (pp. 117-120)

1. (a) $\frac{1}{4}$ (b) $\frac{9}{8}$ (c) $\frac{56}{5}$ or $11\frac{1}{5}$
2. 50
3. (b) 1 m
4. (a) $\frac{1}{24}$ (b) $\frac{4}{33}$
   (a) $\frac{31}{14}$ or $2\frac{3}{14}$
5. (a) 4 yd 1 ft (b) 6 qt 2 c
   (c) 2 lb 3 oz (e) 1 ft 3 in.
6. $\frac{1}{4}$
7. \$312
8. (a) $\frac{6}{5}$ (b) $\frac{2}{7}$
9. 12.5%
10. (a) 264 in. (b) 92 oz (c) 60 c
11. (a) 1 (b) $\frac{1}{5}$
12. (a) 5 lb 4 oz (b) 2 ft 10 in.
    (c) 3 qt 1 pt.
13. \$9.90
14. 29 oz
15. 75%
16. 18 pt

17. 1728
18. 6.75 yd
19. (a) Taylor (b) Morgan (c) 20 c
20. (a) 18 (b) $\frac{3}{2}$ (c) $\frac{27}{14}$
    (d) $\frac{21}{8}$ (e) 4 (f) $\frac{4}{5}$
21. 550 mi/h
22. 2 ft 3 in.
23. $\frac{1}{8}$
24. (a) 1 cm (b) 1 ft
25. 9
26. 20
27. 1:30 p.m.
28. 60 mi/h
29. $\frac{5}{7}$

Workbook Answer Key

US: Exercise 1

1. (a) 12; 12 (b) 5; 10; 10
   (c) 2; 8; 8 (d) 6; 18; 18
2. (a) 6 (b) 5; 15
   (c) 12 (d) 16
   (e) 25 (f) 18
   (g) 8 (h) 42

US: Exercise 2

1. (a) $\frac{1}{9}$ (b) $\frac{1}{6}$; $\frac{1}{12}$
   (c) $\frac{1}{24}$ (d) $\frac{2}{5}$
   (e) $\frac{1}{10}$ (f) $\frac{2}{9}$
   (g) $\frac{3}{8}$ (h) $\frac{1}{9}$

US: Exercise 3

1. (a) $\frac{3}{2}$ (b) 2 (c) 4
   (d) $\frac{5}{2}$ (e) 5 (f) 8
   (g) $\frac{1}{6}$ (h) $\frac{2}{3}$

US: Exercise 4

1. (a) $\frac{7}{8}$ (b) $\frac{19}{24}$ (c) $\frac{1}{2}$
   (d) $\frac{4}{3}$ (e) 1 (f) $\frac{1}{6}$
   (g) $\frac{4}{9}$ (h) $\frac{1}{5}$

US: Exercise 5

1. (a) 0 (b) $\frac{1}{3}$
   (c) $5\frac{1}{2}$ (d) 1
   (e) $\frac{7}{12}$ (f) $2\frac{1}{12}$
   (g) $2\frac{1}{2}$ (h) $\frac{11}{12}$
2. (a) $\frac{5}{8}$ (b) $\frac{2}{3}$ (c) $\frac{1}{6}$
   (d) $\frac{7}{10}$ (e) $18\frac{1}{2}$ (f) $\frac{4}{9}$

US: Exercise 6

1. (a) $\frac{1}{6}$ (b) $\frac{9}{10}$
   (c) $\frac{29}{10}$ (d) $\frac{3}{5}$
   (e) $\frac{1}{6}$ (f) $\frac{3}{2}$
   (g) $\frac{15}{4}$ (h) $\frac{8}{3}$
2. O. $\frac{1}{4}$ I. $1\frac{1}{7}$
   C. $\frac{1}{8}$ E. 1
   S. $\frac{3}{4}$ L. $\frac{1}{2}$
   ISOSCELES

US: Exercise 7

1. 18 lb
2. 350
3. $1050
4. 72

US: Exercise 8

1. $100
2. $192

US: Exercise 9 3rd: Exercise 1

5. (a) 2 cm, 4 cm
   (b) 6 cm, 12 cm

US: Exercise 10 3rd: Exercise 2

2. (a) 15.7 cm (b) 44 cm
   (c) 25.12 m (d) 220 m
3. (a) 81.64 cm (b) 94.2 cm
   (c) 88 m (d) 132 m

US: Exercise 11 **3rd: Exercise 3**

1. (a) 72 cm (b) 51.4 m
2. 17.85 cm
3. 31.4 cm
4. 10π m

US: Exercise 12 **3rd: Exercise 4**

1. (a) 254.34 cm^2
   (b) 78.5 cm^2
   (c) 314 cm^2 (d) 113.04 cm^2
2. (a) 154 cm^2 (b) 616 m^2
   (c) 154 cm^2 (d) 3850 m^2

US: Exercise 13 **3rd: Exercise 5**

1. 314 cm^2
2. 78.5 cm^2
3. (a) 77 cm^2 (b) 308 cm^2

US: Exercise 14 **3rd: Exercise 6**

1. (a) 154 cm^2 (b) 115.5 cm^2 (c) 192.5 cm^2
2. (a) 10π cm^2 (b) 50π cm^2 (c) 4π cm^2
3. 42 cm^2
4. 86 cm^2
5. 25 cm^2

US: Exercise 15 **3rd: Exercise 7**

1. (a) 77 cm^2 (b) 196 cm^2 (c) 273 cm^2
2. (a) 78.5 cm^2 (b) 120 cm^2 (c) 198.5 cm^2
3. (a) 25.12 cm^2 (b) 40 cm^2 (c) 65.12 cm^2
4. (a) 77 m^2 (b) 19.25 m^2 (c) 57.75 m^2
5. (a) 16 cm^2 (b) 3.14 cm^2 (c) 12.86 cm^2
6. (a) 700 cm^2 (b) 314 cm^2 (c) 386 cm^2

US: Exercise 16 **3rd: Exercise 8**

1. 53.7 m
2. 109.12 cm^2
3. 871 cm^2, 114.2 cm
4. 164.5 cm^2, 87.1 cm

US : Exercise 17 **3rd: Exercise 9**

1. (a) 16 (b) 12 (c) 40
   (d) $\frac{1}{5}$ (e) $\frac{1}{10}$
2. (a) Cars (b) 2000 (c) 10,000
   (d) $\frac{2}{25}$ (e) $\frac{8}{25}$
3. (a) 250 (b) 200 (c) 500
   (d) 20% (e) 3
4. (a) $\frac{1}{8}$ (b) \$40 (c) $\frac{1}{2}$
   (d) 25% (e) 1 : 4

US: Exercise 18 **3rd: Exercise 10**

1. Motorcycles $\frac{1}{5}$, Cars $\frac{2}{5}$,
   US: Trucks $\frac{3}{20}$ 3rd: Lorries $\frac{3}{20}$
2. (a) $\frac{3}{8}$ (b) $\frac{1}{4}$ (c) $\frac{1}{8}$
   (d) 150 (e) 100
3. (a) $\frac{1}{2}$ (b) $\frac{2}{9}$ (c) 20
   (d) 30 (e) 10
4. (a) Chocolate (b) $\frac{2}{5}$
   (c) 30% (d) 20% (e) 160

US: Exercise 19 **3rd: Exercise 11**

1. Vacuum cleaner 15%, Fan 10%, Oven 35%
2. (a) 15% (b) 25% (c) 40%
   (d) 12 (e) 16
3. (a) 4 (b) 10% (c) 6 kg
   (d) 20 kg (e) 10 kg
4. (a) $\frac{7}{20}$ (b) 25% (c) 15%
   (d) 120 (e) 42

Review 1

1. 10,000
2. 247,000
3. 0.106
4. 2.85
5. (a) 3 (b) 9
6. $\frac{1}{8}$
7. 37.5%
8. US: (a) $\frac{4}{5}$ (b) $\frac{23}{32}$ 3rd: 1 h 25 min

9. 1.64 m
10. 35%
11. $680
12. 20 min
13. 40
14. 36
15. 50
16. $5
17. 116 cm^2
18. 49 cm
19. 957 cm^2
20. 12π cm
21. 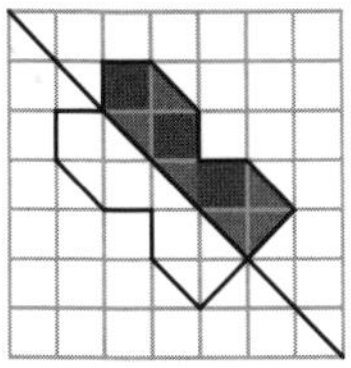
22. (a) 30 kg (b) 8 : 5 (c) $\frac{3}{5}$
23. $6.40
24. $\frac{9}{20}$
25. $135
26. 55

Review 2

1. 5
2. (a) 10 (b) 4
3. (a) 29 (b) 8
4. 150
5. $\frac{3}{8}$
6. $\frac{4}{7}$
7. 3.71
8. 3
9. $9.75
10. 15
11. 1200 ml
12. 125
13. $2200
14. $1800
15. 16 min
16. (a) $\frac{3}{4}$ (b) 13
17. $(120 - 3x)$ kg
18. 28 m^2
19. 161 cm^2
20. 91.4 cm
21. 64 cm^2
23. (a) $70 (b) $610
24. 110 cm
25. 125
26. 160
27. 3:50 pm

US: 28. (a) $6\frac{1}{8}$ (b) $3\frac{7}{10}$

US: Exercise 20 3rd: Exercise 12

1. (a) 64 cm^3 (b) 88 cm^3
   (c) 56 cm^3 (d) 88 cm^3
2. (a) 60 (b) 240
3. (a) 10 cm (b) 6 cm

US : Exercise 21 3rd: Exercise 13

1. (a) 1.28 ℓ (b) 2.4 ℓ
   (c) 3.2 ℓ (d) 0.48 ℓ
2. 2.4 ℓ
3. 4.8 ℓ
4. 42 cm
5. 40 cm

US : Exercise 22 3rd: Exercise 14

1. 7200 cm^3
2. 10.25 ℓ
3. 1000 cm^3
4. 20 cm
5. 18

US : Exercise 23 3rd: Exercise 15

1. $1\frac{1}{2}$ min or 1 min 30 s
2. 16 min
3. 7 min
4. 32 cm

Review 3

1. 0.12
2. 5.81

3. (a) $\frac{5}{8}$ (b) US: $\frac{9}{40}$ 3rd: $\frac{2}{15}$
4. 2 h 45 min
5. 90
6. 2 : 3
7. 4.5%
8. 252 g
9. 8:10 a.m.
10. 18
11. 1.64 m
12. $\frac{5}{16}$
13. $36
14. 13
15. 3 : 19
16. $150
17. 5 min
18. 3 h
19. $(45$x$ + 50)
20. 83 cm^2
21. 9π cm
22. 24 cm
23. (c)
24. (a) $450 (b) $292
25. $90
26. $24

Review 4

1. 507.904
2. (a) 4 (b) 10
3. (a) 8 (b) 7
4. 1.7 ℓ
5. 6 ℓ
6. 6
7. $23
8. 37.1 kg
9. $160
10. 7 : 6 : 4
11. $108
12. 28.5 cm^2
13. 36 cm
14. 45
15. 36 cm^2
16. C
17. (a) 25% (b) 15% (c) $400
18. 18 km

US: Exercise 24 3rd: Exercise 16

1. 136°
2. 32°
3. 105°
4. 38°
5. 34°
6. 135°
7. 110°
8. 28°
9. 70°
10. 52°
11. 66°
12. 125°

US : Exercise 25 3rd: Exercise 17

1. 68°
2. 38°
3. 110°
4. 58°
5. 30°
6. 109°
7. 130°
8. 35°
9. 58°
10. 30°
11. 76°
12. 70°

Review 5

1. (a) 70,000 (b) 10
2. 100,000
3. 34%
4. $2.25
5. 75%
6. $0.80
7. 750
8. $10.50
9. $240
10. 98
11. 35%
12. 5 : 11
13. 200
14. 45 min
15. 75 km/h
16. 8a cm

17. 78 cm
18. 400 cm^2
19. 21,000 cm^3
20. 50°
21. (a) diagram of triangle with □C = 6 cm, □B = 5 cm, angle □ = 60°
    (b) 5.6 cm
22. (a) \$2000 (b) \$400 (c) $\frac{2}{5}$
23. \$2.40
24. \$60

Review 6

1. 24
2. 7
3. 8:35 a.m.
4. 4.4
5. \$5.40
6. 39
7. 250 m/min
8. \$600
9. 40%
10. \$247.20
11. 70
12. US: 18 in. 3rd: 18 cm
13. \$80
14. \$200
15. $\frac{1}{2}$h or 30 min
16. US: 44 in. 3rd: 44 cm
17. 8π m^2
18. US: 50 ft^2 3rd: 50 cm^2
19. 8 min
20. 69°
21. 120°
22. 3 : 4
23. (a) 25% (b) \$220
    (c) \$66 (d) 5 : 4
24. \$15
25. 150

Review 7

1. 4.53
2. 37
3. 36
4. 397.8
5. US: $\frac{5}{6}$ 3rd: 140 min
6. 3.05 kg
7. \$40
8. 420
9. \$150
10. 10
11. $\frac{4}{9}$
12. 4 : 9
13. 240
14. 100
15. 22 km
16. 6:45 a.m.
17. $1\frac{2}{3}$
18. \$$(6x + 18)$
19. 33 cm
20. 18 cm
21. 25°
22. 15°
23. 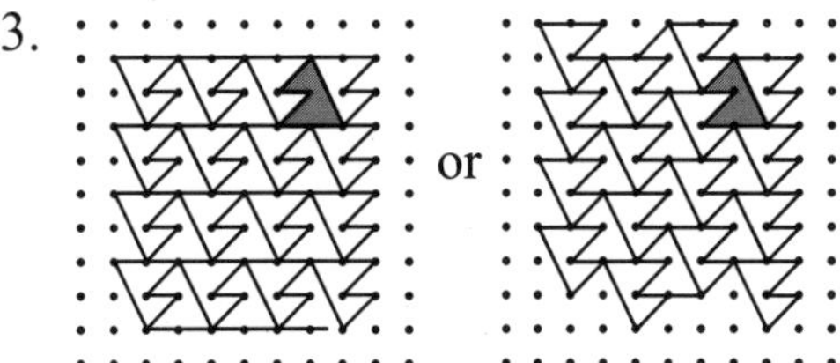

24. (a) 125 ℓ (b) 10 min
25. 45
26. 8:05 a.m.
27. $\frac{1}{10}$
28. (b) 0.116
29. $\frac{3}{25}$
30. 52